Exploring Data

Exploring Data was prepared under the auspices of the American Statistical Association—National Council of Teachers of Mathematics Joint Committee on the Curriculum in Statistics and Probability.

This book is part of the Quantitative Literacy Project, which was funded in part by the National Science Foundation.

Exploring Data

James M. Landwehr
AT&T Bell Laboratories
Murray Hill, New Jersey

Ann E. Watkins
Los Angeles Pierce College
Woodland Hills, California

DALE SEYMOUR PUBLICATIONS

Cover Design: John Edeen
Technical Art: Pat Rogondino

This publication was prepared as part of the American Statistical
Association Project—Quantitative Literacy—with partial support of the
National Science Foundation Grant No. DPE-8317656. Any opinions,
findings, conclusions, or recommendations expressed in this publication
are those of the authors and do not necessarily represent the views of
the National Science Foundation.

ISBN 0-86651-321-3
Order Number DS01617

DALE
SEYMOUR
PUBLICATIONS
P.O. BOX 10888
PALO ALTO, CA 94303

defghij-MA-89321098

CONTENTS

PREFACE

Exploring Data is an introduction to statistics. In addition to learning the most up-to-date statistical techniques, you will have an opportunity to practice techniques in other areas of mathematics.

Familiar statistical topics, such as tables of data, the mean (average), and scatter plots, are included in this book. Less familiar topics, such as the median, stem-and-leaf plots, box plots, and smoothing, are also included. All of these techniques are part of a new emphasis in statistics called *data analysis.* Data analysis de-emphasizes the use of algebraic formulas for analyzing data. Instead, data analysis stresses the importance of organizing and displaying data so that it reveals its patterns and surprises. The techniques of data analysis are easy to use and are frequently graphical.

John W. Tukey, an influential statistician who recently retired from Princeton University and AT&T Bell Laboratories, was the leader in this new approach to statistics. He first published these techniques in the 1960s and 1970s. Nowhere else in your study of mathematics will you learn methods developed so recently.

The techniques in this material encourage you to ask questions about data. This is an important part of data analysis. By using these methods you will be able to interpret data that are interesting and important to you.

The authors gratefully acknowledge the inspiration and leadership of Jim Swift in the preparation of materials on data analysis for secondary students.

I. LINE PLOTS

The 1984 Winter Olympics were held in Sarajevo, Yugoslavia. The table below lists the total number of gold, silver, and bronze medals won, by country.

Country	Total Medals	Country	Total Medals
Austria	1	Italy	2
Canada	4	Japan	1
Czechoslovakia	6	Liechtenstein	2
Finland	13	Norway	9
France	3	Sweden	8
Germany, East	24	Switzerland	5
Germany, West	4	USSR	25
Great Britain	1	United States	8
		Yugoslavia	1

Source: *The World Almanac and Book of Facts*, 1985 edition.

Let's make a *line plot* of these data. First, make a horizontal line.

Then, put a scale of numbers on this line using a ruler. Since the smallest number of medals is 1 and the largest is 25, the scale might run from 0 to 25 as shown below.

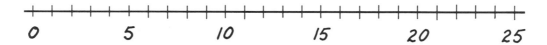

The first country, Austria, won one medal. To represent Austria, put an X above the line at the number 1.

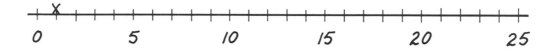

Continuing this way with the other countries, we can complete the line plot as shown below.

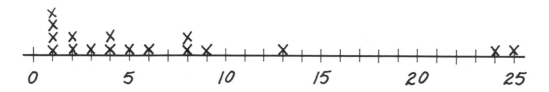

From a line plot, features of the data become apparent that were not as apparent from the list. These features include:

- *Outliers* — data values that are substantially larger or smaller than the other values
- *Clusters* — isolated groups of points
- *Gaps* — large spaces between points

It is also easy to spot the largest and smallest values from a line plot. If you see a cluster, try to decide if its members have anything special in common. For example, in the previous line plot the two largest values form a cluster. They are the USSR and East Germany — both eastern European countries. These two values are quite a bit larger than the rest, so we could also consider these points to be outliers.

Often, we would like to know the location of a particular point of interest. For these data, we might want to know how well the United States did compared to the other countries.

Discussion Questions

1. How many countries won only one medal?
2. How many countries won ten or more medals?
3. Do the countries seem to fall into clusters on the line plot?
4. Describe how the United States compares with the other countries.
5. In this book, you will often be asked to "describe what you learned from looking at the plot." Try to do this now with the plot of medal winners, then read the following sample.

> Seventeen countries won medals in the 1984 Winter Olympics. Two countries, the USSR with 25 and East Germany with 24, won many more medals than the next country, Finland, with 13. The remaining countries were all clustered, with from 1 to 9 medals each. The United States won 8 medals, more than 11 countries but not many in comparison to the leaders. One noticeable feature about these 17 countries is that, with the exception of the United States, Canada, and Japan, they are all in Europe.
>
> The list does not say how many countries did not win any medals. This might be interesting to find out.

Writing descriptions is probably new to you. When you look at the plot, jot down any observations you make and any questions that occur to you. Look specifically for outliers, clusters, and the other features we mentioned. Then organize and write your paragraphs as if you were composing them for your English teacher. The ability to organize, summarize, and communicate numerical information is a necessary skill in many occupations and is similar to your work with science projects and science laboratory reports.

Application 1

Rock Albums

The following list of the top 10 record albums in the first five months of 1985 is based on *Billboard* magazine reports.

Artist	Title	Total Points
Bruce Springsteen	"Born in the U.S.A."	183
Madonna	"Like a Virgin"	149
Phil Collins	"No Jacket Required"	108
John Fogerty	"Centerfield"	97
Wham!	"Make It Big"	97
Soundtrack	"Beverly Hills Cop"	93
Tina Turner	"Private Dancer"	69
Prince	"Purple Rain"	59
Foreigner	"Agent Provocateur"	54
USA for Africa	"We Are the World"	49

Source: *Los Angeles Times*, May 25, 1985.

The total points were calculated by giving 10 points for each week an album was number 1 on the *Billboard* charts, 9 points for each week it was number 2, 8 points for each week it was number 3, and so forth.

1. If a record was number 1 for 3 weeks, number 2 for 5 weeks, and number 3 for 2 weeks, how many total points would it have?

2. How many points does a record earn by being number 5 for 1 week?

3. If a record was number 4 for 3 weeks and number 5 for 1 week, how many total points would it have?

4. Find two ways for a record to earn 25 points.

5. There were about 21 weeks in the first five months of 1985. Find a way for "Born in the U.S.A." to earn 183 points in these 21 weeks.

The following line plot was constructed from these data.

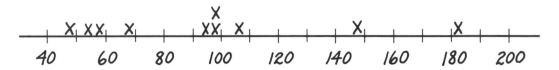

6. Which record(s) is an outlier?

7. Do the records seem to cluster into more than one group?

8. List the records in the lowest group.

9. List the records in the next lowest group.

10. Write a description of what you learned from studying this plot.

3

Causes of Death

The United States Public Health Service issues tables giving death rates by cause of death. These are broken down by age group, and the table below is for people 15-24 years of age. It gives death rates per 100,000 population for 16 leading causes of death. As an example, a death rate of 1.7 for leukemia means that out of 100,000 people in the United States aged 15-24, we can expect 1.7 of them will die annually from leukemia.

Cause of Death	Death Rate (per 100,000 people aged 15-24 per year)
heart diseases	2.9
leukemia	1.7
cancers of lymph and blood other than leukemia	1.0
other cancers	3.6
strokes	1.0
motor vehicle accidents	44.8
other accidents	16.9
chronic lung diseases	0.3
pneumonia and influenza	0.8
diabetes	0.3
liver diseases	0.3
suicide	12.3
homicide	15.6
kidney diseases	0.3
birth defects	1.4
blood poisoning	0.2

Source: National Center for Health Statistics, Monthly Vital Statistics Report, August 1983.

1. Of 100,000 people aged 15-24, how many would you expect to die annually from pneumonia and influenza?

2. Of 1,000,000 people aged 15-24, how many would you expect to die annually from pneumonia and influenza?

3. Suppose there are 200,000 people, and 3 die from a certain cause. What is the death rate per 100,000 people?

4. Of 250,000 people aged 15-24, about how many would you expect to die annually from motor vehicle accidents?

5. Construct a line plot of these data. To avoid crowding when plotting the X's, round each death rate to the nearest whole number.

6. Which cause of death is an outlier?

7. Which three causes of death are in the cluster below the outlier?

8. Which medical problem has the largest death rate?

9. Write a summary of the information communicated by the line plot. Include a list of any questions you have about the data. (For example, in which category are drug overdoses included?)

10. (For class discussion) Suppose you want to reduce the total death rate for 15-24 year olds, and you have $10 million to spend. How would you spend it? On medical research, medical treatment, or in some other way?

Line Plots — Summary

Line plots are a quick, simple way to organize data. They work best when there are fewer than 25 numbers. With many more, the plot starts to look crowded.

From a line plot it is easy to spot the largest and smallest values, outliers, clusters, and gaps in the data. It is also possible to find the relative position of particular points of interest. Sometimes you can notice outliers, clusters, and gaps from the table of data. However, the line plot is easy to make and has several advantages. It makes it easy to spot these features, it gives a graphical picture of the relative sizes of the numbers, and it helps you to make sure that you aren't missing any important information.

When making line plots, be sure to place the X's for values that are approximately the same on top of each other rather than crowding them in. It is also usual to number the scale in multiples of 1, 5, 10, 100, or some other round number.

Suggestions for Student Projects

Collect data on one of the ideas listed below or on your own topic. Make a line plot of the data and write a summary of the information displayed by the plot.

1. heights of students in your class

2. grades on your math tests this year

3. grades on the last test for the members of your class

4. ages of the mothers of students in your class

5. number of hours of television you watch each day for two weeks

6. number of miles each student drives in a week

7. number of students in your class born in each of the 12 months (On the number line, 1 would represent January, 2 would represent February, and so forth.)

II. STEM-AND-LEAF PLOTS

The table below gives the amounts of calories, fat, carbohydrates (sugar and starch), and sodium (salt) in each serving of various fast food items. Fat and carbohydrates are measured in grams; sodium in milligrams.

Item	Calories	Fat (gm)	Carbohydrates (gm)	Sodium (mg)
HAMBURGERS				
Burger King Whopper	660	41	49	1083
Jack-in-the-Box Jumbo Jack	538	28	44	1007
McDonald's Big Mac	591	33	46	963
Wendy's Old Fashioned	413	22	29	708
SANDWICHES				
Roy Rogers Roast Beef	356	12	34	610
Burger King Chopped-Beef Steak	445	13	50	966
Hardee's Roast Beef	351	17	32	765
Arby's Roast Beef	370	15	36	869
FISH				
Long John Silver's	483	27	27	1333
Arthur Treacher's Original	439	27	27	421
McDonald's Filet-O-Fish	383	18	38	613
Burger King Whaler	584	34	50	968
CHICKEN				
Kentucky-Fried Chicken Snack Box	405	21	16	728
Arthur Treacher's Original Chicken	409	23	25	580
SPECIALTY ENTREES				
Wendy's Chili	266	9	29	1190
Pizza Hut Pizza Supreme	506	15	64	1281
Jack-in-the-Box Taco	429	26	34	926

Source: *Consumer Reports*, September 1979.

Suppose you decide to order a McDonald's Big Mac. It contains 33 grams of fat. How does this compare to the other items? By looking at the table, about all we can see is that it does not have the most fat nor the least. So that we can get a better picture of the grams of fat per serving, let's make a stem-and-leaf plot.

First, find the smallest value and the largest value.

The smallest value is 9 for Wendy's Chili and the largest is 41 for the Burger King Whopper.

The smallest value, 9, has a 0 in the ten's place and the largest value, 41, has a 4 in the ten's place. Therefore, we choose the *stems* to be the digits from 0 to 4.

Second, write these stems vertically with a line to their right.

```
0 |
1 |
2 |
3 |
4 |
```

Third, separate each value into a stem and a leaf and put the leaves on the plot to the right of the stem.

For example, the first value in the list is 41, for a Burger King Whopper. Its stem is 4 and its leaf is 1. It is placed on the plot as follows:

```
0 |
1 |
2 |
3 |
4 | 1
```

The second value in the list is 28. Its stem is 2 and its leaf is 8. Now the plot looks as shown below.

```
0 |
1 |
2 | 8
3 |
4 | 1
```

Continuing in this way gives the following plot:

```
0 | 9
1 | 2 3 7 5 8 5
2 | 8 2 7 7 1 3 6
3 | 3 4
4 | 1
```

Next, on a new plot arrange the leaves so they are ordered from smallest value to largest. (This final step is often omitted.)

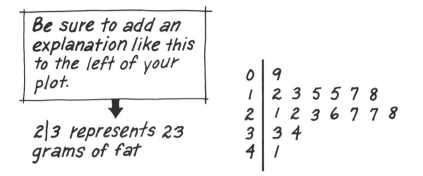

```
0 | 9
1 | 2 3 5 5 7 8
2 | 1 2 3 6 7 7 8
3 | 3 4
4 | 1
```

Be sure to add an explanation like this to the left of your plot.

2|3 represents 23 grams of fat

The plot shows that most of the food items have grams of fat in the 10's and 20's and that there are a few large values. The McDonald's Big Mac with 33 grams has one of the larger amounts of fat.

If we rotate the stem-and-leaf plot 90° counterclockwise, we get a plot that resembles a bar graph or histogram.

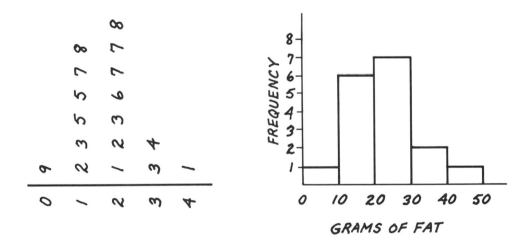

The stem-and-leaf plot is often better than the bar graph or histogram because it is easier to construct and all the original data values are displayed.

It is sometimes worthwhile to label specific items. For example, we might want to label the smallest value, the largest value, and a value of special interest such as McDonald's Big Mac. This is shown below.

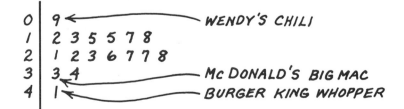

```
0 | 9  ←———————— WENDY'S CHILI
1 | 2 3 5 5 7 8
2 | 1 2 3 6 7 7 8
3 | 3 4 ←———————— McDONALD'S BIG MAC
4 | 1 ←———————— BURGER KING WHOPPER
```

9

Also, it is sometimes interesting to replace the leaves in the stem-and-leaf plot by symbols identifying the items. For example, replace each of the four hamburger leaves with an *H*, each of the four sandwich leaves with an *S*, each of the four fish leaves with an *F*, each of the two chicken leaves with a *C*, and each of the three special entree leaves with an *O* (for other). Replacing the leaves by symbols gives the following:

```
0 | O
1 | S S S O S F
2 | C H C O F F H
3 | H F
4 | H
```

When writing a description of a stem-and-leaf plot, look for the same features that you looked for with a line plot:

- largest and smallest values

- outliers

- clusters

- gaps

- the relative position of any item important to you

Our description of what we learned about fat in the fast food items from the stem-and-leaf plots follows:

There are no outliers separated far from the rest nor any large internal gaps among these values. Of these fast foods, the type that is generally highest in fat is the hamburger, which has three of the highest four values. One hamburger is lower in fat than the others and lies in about the middle of all these values; it is Wendy's Old Fashioned. Some possible reasons for its lower value are: it might be smaller than the others, it might be made from meat with a lower fat content, or it might be cooked differently.

From the data, the type of food that is second highest in fat is fish; the values are only slightly smaller than those for hamburgers. Again, one fish value, McDonald's Filet-O-Fish, is smaller than the other fish values. Although we generally think of fish as having a lot less fat than beef, perhaps these fish items are all fried and therefore high in fat.

The type of food lowest in fat is the roast beef sandwich, and chicken falls near the middle in these data. It is surprising that both the lowest and highest items are beef, but perhaps the sandwich is lowest because it is not fried. The other specialty items are spread throughout the data, but they include the single lowest item, Wendy's Chili. Is it just a coincidence that the hamburger that was lowest in fat was also from Wendy's?

When analyzing data throughout this book, you will need to examine the plots and to think about other information you may have from outside mathematics that can help to interpret the results. Sometimes, this process will lead to questions and possibilities about the problem that cannot be answered just from the data.

The stem-and-leaf plot shows the shape of the set of data more clearly than a line plot. The "shape" of a set of data is called its *distribution*. For example, some common types of distribution follow:

```
3 | 4                      2 | 5 5 8
4 | 6 9 9                  3 | 2 3 4 4 5 9
5 | 2 4 4 5 5 9            4 | 6 7 7
6 | 1 1 7                  5 | 4
7 | 8                      6 | 1 1 3 8
                           7 | 0 1 3 4 4 5 6 8 8
                           8 | 2 3 5 5

  MOUND-SHAPED               U-SHAPED


3 | 4                      3 | 2 2 3 8
4 | 7 8                    4 | 1 5 7
5 | 2 2 3                  5 | 0 4 4 9
6 | 1 1 2 4 4 5 7 8        6 | 1 1 5 7
7 | 0 1 2 2 2 3 6 8 8 9 9  7 | 3 6 8 8 9

  J-SHAPED                 RECTANGULAR-SHAPED
```

The mound-shaped distribution, sometimes called bell-shaped, is a shape that occurs often. The data values are fairly symmetrical, with lows balancing the highs. If the data follow a U-shaped distribution, it may be because there are really two underlying groups, each of which is mound-shaped, corresponding to the two peaks. Thus, when a U-shaped plot is observed, it is a good idea to see if there is any reason to treat the observations as two separate groups.

The J-shaped plot or the backward J-shaped plot does not occur as often as the first two types. Typically, it occurs because it is impossible to have observations above (or below) a particular limit. In the example above, this limit might be 80. In some problems, there is a lower limit of 0. If you observe a J-shaped plot, try to determine if there is a limit, what it is, and why it is there. For a rectangular-shaped distribution, sometimes called flat or uniform, there are often both lower and upper limits with the data values spread evenly between them. For the previous example, the limits might be 30 and 80. As with the J-shaped plot, you should try to understand if there are limits to the possible values of the data, and what the limits might mean.

Discussion Questions

1. Make a stem-and-leaf plot of the grams of carbohydrates in the fast food items. Label the smallest value, the largest value, and McDonald's Big Mac.

2. Make another stem-and-leaf plot of the grams of carbohydrates, but replace the leaves by the symbols:
   H for hamburger
   S for sandwich
   F for fish
   C for chicken
   O for other

3. Write a description of the information displayed in the stem-and-leaf plot of the grams of carbohydrates. Mention any interesting patterns. How does this plot compare to the one for fat?

4. All of the fast food information was given on a per item basis. However, the sizes of the items are different. Do you think this should be taken into account? How might you do this? Should price also be considered?

5. In judging fast food items, which is most important to you: calories, fat, carbohydrates, or sodium?

6. Give an example of data that are distributed a) U-shaped. b) mound-shaped. c) J-shaped. d) rectangular-shaped.

Application 3

Ages of U.S. Presidents at Their Death

The table below lists the presidents of the United States and the ages at which they died.

Washington	67	Filmore	74	Roosevelt	60
Adams	90	Pierce	64	Taft	72
Jefferson	83	Buchanan	77	Wilson	67
Madison	85	Lincoln	56	Harding	57
Monroe	73	Johnson	66	Coolidge	60
Adams	80	Grant	63	Hoover	90
Jackson	78	Hayes	70	Roosevelt	63
Van Buren	79	Garfield	49	Truman	88
Harrison	68	Arthur	57	Eisenhower	78
Tyler	71	Cleveland	71	Kennedy	46
Polk	53	Harrison	67	Johnson	64
Taylor	65	McKinley	58		

1. Make a stem-and-leaf plot of the ages using these stems.

$$\begin{array}{r|l} 4 & \\ 5 & \\ 6 & \\ 7 & \\ 8 & \\ 9 & \end{array}$$

2. How many presidents died in their forties or fifties?

3. Who lived to be the oldest?

4. Label the four presidents who were assassinated.

5. What is the shape of this distribution?

6. Write a one-paragraph description of the information shown in the stem-and-leaf plot, including information about the presidents who were assassinated.

Application 4

Thunderstorms

The table below lists 81 U.S. cities with the number of days per year with thunderstorms.

Area	Number of Days	Area	Number of Days	Area	Number of Days
Akron, OH	39	Detroit, MI	33	Oklahoma City, OK	51
Albany, NY	28	El Paso, TX	36	Omaha, NE	51
Albuquerque, NM	43	Fargo, ND	30	Orlando, FL	85
Anchorage, AK	1	Fresno, CA	5	Philadelphia, PA	42
Atlanta, GA	50	Grand Rapids, MI	37	Phoenix, AZ	20
Austin, TX	40	Great Falls, MT	27	Pittsburgh, PA	35
Bakersfield, CA	3	Hartford, CT	28	Portland, ME	20
Baltimore, MD	24	Honolulu, HI	7	Portland, OR	7
Baton Rouge, LA	80	Houston, TX	59	Providence, RI	21
Beaumont, TX	63	Indianapolis, IN	47	Raleigh, NC	45
Biloxi, MS	80	Kansas City, MO	50	Richmond, VA	37
Birmingham, AL	65	Las Vegas, NV	13	Rochester, NY	29
Boise, ID	15	Little Rock, AR	56	Sacramento, CA	5
Boston, MA	19	Louisville, KY	52	Salt Lake City, UT	41
Buffalo, NY	30	Los Angeles, CA	6	San Antonio, TX	35
Burlington, VT	27	Manchester, NH	24	San Diego, CA	3
Charleston, SC	58	Memphis, TN	50	San Francisco, CA	2
Charleston, WV	45	Miami, FL	71	Seattle, WA	6
Chicago, IL	36	Milwaukee, WI	37	Shreveport, LA	58
Cincinnati, OH	52	Minneapolis, MN	36	Sioux Falls, SD	47
Cleveland, OH	38	Mobile, AL	86	St. Louis, MO	43
Columbia, SC	52	Nashville, TN	52	Tampa, FL	91
Columbus, OH	36	Nassau-Suffolk, NY	18	Tucson, AZ	28
Corpus Christi, TX	32	Newark, NJ	25	Tulsa, OK	53
Dallas, TX	41	New Orleans, LA	73	Washington, DC	28
Denver, CO	38	New York, NY	18	Wichita, KS	53
Des Moines, IA	55	Norfolk, VA	36	Wilmington, DE	30

Source: United States Weather Bureau.

14

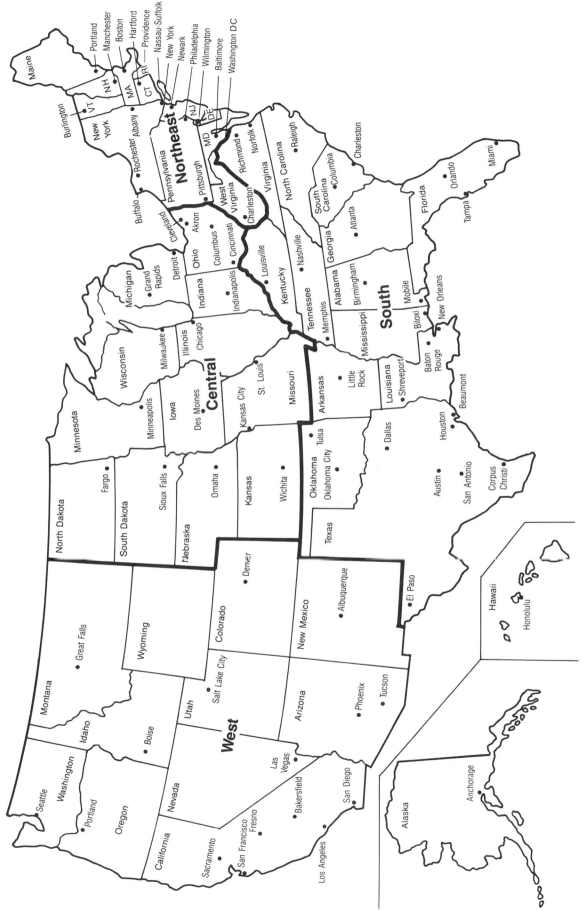

A stem-and-leaf plot of the number of days of thunderstorms is shown below. Notice that the stem for numbers less than 10 is 0.

```
0 | 1 2 3 3 5 5 6 6 7 7

1 | 3 5 8 8 9

2 | 0 0 1 4 4 5 7 7 8 8 8 8 9

3 | 0 0 0 2 3 5 5 6 6 6 6 7 7 7 8 8 9

4 | 0 1 1 2 3 3 5 5 7 7

5 | 0 0 0 1 1 2 2 2 2 3 3 5 6 8 8 9

6 | 3 5

7 | 1 3

8 | 0 0 5 6

9 | 1
```

6|3 REPRESENTS
63 THUNDERSTORMS
PER YEAR

1. How does your city, or the city nearest you, compare to the other cities?

2. Which five cities have the largest number of days with thunderstorms? What do these five cities have in common?

3. The map on page 15 shows the United States divided into four regions: west, south, central, and northeast. Make a stem-and-leaf plot, replacing each city with the label for its location:

   W for WEST
   S for SOUTH
   C for CENTRAL
   N for NORTHEAST

4. Write a summary of what you can see in this stem-and-leaf plot.

Soft Drinks

The table below shows the number of *gallons* of soft drinks sold per person in 1977 for each state.

State	Gallons per Person	State	Gallons per Person
Alabama (AL)	36.8	Nebraska (NE)	32.9
Alaska (AK)	29.5	Nevada (NV)	34.5
Arizona (AZ)	29.1	New Hampshire (NH)	28.4
Arkansas (AR)	33.3	New Jersey (NJ)	28.7
California (CA)	32.2	New Mexico (NM)	28.7
Colorado (CO)	30.0	New York (NY)	31.7
Connecticut (CT)	31.3	North Carolina (NC)	39.9
Delaware (DE)	32.5	North Dakota (ND)	23.2
Florida (FL)	39.7	Ohio (OH)	34.1
Georgia (GA)	39.4	Oklahoma (OK)	31.0
Hawaii (HI)	31.3	Oregon (OR)	23.8
Idaho (ID)	20.7	Pennsylvania (PA)	26.5
Illinois (IL)	33.2	Rhode Island (RI)	28.5
Indiana (IN)	28.8	South Carolina (SC)	39.1
Iowa (IA)	29.0	South Dakota (SD)	25.5
Kansas (KS)	35.9	Tennessee (TN)	36.4
Kentucky (KY)	35.3	Texas (TX)	35.9
Louisiana (LA)	36.7	Utah (UT)	28.0
Maine (ME)	29.2	Vermont (VT)	26.6
Maryland (MD)	34.9	Virginia (VA)	38.3
Massachusetts (MA)	31.6	Washington (WA)	25.1
Michigan (MI)	33.4	Washington, D.C. (DC)	36.0
Minnesota (MN)	33.0	West Virginia (WV)	34.2
Mississippi (MS)	38.2	Wisconsin (WI)	28.8
Missouri (MO)	36.4	Wyoming (WY)	20.6
Montana (MT)	23.3		

Source: *Beverage World*, March 1978.

(After each state is its two-letter postal abbreviation. In some applications we will use these for identifying the states, so you may need to refer back to this list to check any that are unfamiliar.)

1. How many ounces are in a gallon?

2. In Alabama, 36.8 gallons were sold per person. How many ounces were sold per person? How many 12-ounce cans would 36.8 gallons fill?

3. For the number of gallons per person in your state, find the equivalent number of 12-ounce cans of soft drinks.

4. These data are different from previous sets of data since the numbers contain decimals. The values go from 20.6 to 39.9, so we choose the stems to be 20, 21, 22, ..., 39. Copy and complete this stem-and-leaf plot of the gallons per person. The plot has been started with the values for Alabama and Alaska.

```
20 |
21 |
22 |
23 |
24 |
25 |
26 |
27 |
28 |
29 | 5
30 |
31 |
32 |
33 |
34 |
35 |
36 | 8
37 |
38 |
39 |
```

20|6 REPRESENTS
20.6 GALLONS

5. Label your state.

6. Label the states that have the lowest soft drink consumption.

7. Label the states that have the highest soft drink consumption.

8. Which region of the country consumes the most soft drinks per person? What is your explanation for this?

9. (For class discussion) How could these data have been collected?

Back-to-Back Stem-and-Leaf Plots and Spreading Out Stem-and-Leaf Plots

Sometimes we want to compare two sets of data. For example, look at the following tables that contain the home run leaders for the National League and American League from 1921 to 1985.

	Home Run Leaders			
Year	National League	HR	American League	HR
1921	George Kelly, New York	23	Babe Ruth, New York	59
1922	Rogers Hornsby, St. Louis	42	Ken Williams, St. Louis	39
1923	Cy Williams, Philadelphia	41	Babe Ruth, New York	41
1924	Jacques Foumier, Brooklyn	27	Babe Ruth, New York	46
1925	Rogers Hornsby, St. Louis	39	Bob Meusel, New York	33
1926	Hack Wilson, Chicago	21	Babe Ruth, New York	47
1927	Hack Wilson, Chicago Cy Williams, Philadelphia	30	Babe Ruth, New York	60
1928	Hack Wilson, Chicago Jim Bottomley, St. Louis	31	Babe Ruth, New York	54
1929	Charles Klein, Philadelphia	43	Babe Ruth, New York	46
1930	Hack Wilson, Chicago	56	Babe Ruth, New York	49
1931	Charles Klein, Philadelphia	31	Babe Ruth, New York Lou Gehrig, New York	46
1932	Charles Klein, Philadelphia Mel Ott, New York	38	Jimmy Foxx, Philadelphia	58
1933	Charles Klein, Philadelphia	28	Jimmy Foxx, Philadelphia	48
1934	Rip Collins, St. Louis Mel Ott, New York	35	Lou Gehrig, New York	49
1935	Walter Berger, Boston	34	Jimmy Foxx, Philadelphia Hank Greenberg, Detroit	36
1936	Mel Ott, New York	33	Lou Gehrig, New York	49
1937	Mel Ott, New York Joe Medwick, St. Louis	31	Joe DiMaggio, New York	46
1938	Mel Ott, New York	36	Hank Greenberg, Detroit	58
1939	John Mize, St. Louis	28	Jimmy Foxx, Boston	35
1940	John Mize, St. Louis	43	Hank Greenberg, Detroit	41
1941	Dolph Camilli, Brooklyn	34	Ted Williams, Boston	37
1942	Mel Ott, New York	30	Ted Williams, Boston	36
1943	Bill Nicholson, Chicago	29	Rudy York, Detroit	34
1944	Bill Nicholson, Chicago	33	Nick Etten, New York	22
1945	Tommy Holmes, Boston	28	Vern Stephens, St. Louis	24
1946	Ralph Kiner, Pittsburgh	23	Hank Greenberg, Detroit	44
1947	Ralph Kiner, Pittsburgh John Mize, New York	51	Ted Williams, Boston	32
1948	Ralph Kiner, Pittsburgh John Mize, New York	40	Joe DiMaggio, New York	39
1949	Ralph Kiner, Pittsburgh	54	Ted Williams, Boston	43
1950	Ralph Kiner, Pittsburgh	47	Al Rosen, Cleveland	37
1951	Ralph Kiner, Pittsburgh	42	Gus Zernial, Chicago-Philadelphia	33
1952	Ralph Kiner, Pittsburgh Hank Sauer, Chicago	37	Larry Doby, Cleveland	32

Source: *The World Almanac and Book of Facts,* 1985 edition.

Home Run Leaders

Year	National League	HR	American League	HR
1953	Ed Mathews, Milwaukee	47	Al Rosen, Cleveland	43
1954	Ted Kluszewski, Cincinnati	49	Larry Doby, Cleveland	32
1955	Willie Mays, New York	51	Mickey Mantle, New York	37
1956	Duke Snider, Brooklyn	43	Mickey Mantle, New York	52
1957	Hank Aaron, Milwaukee	44	Roy Sievers, Washington	42
1958	Ernie Banks, Chicago	47	Mickey Mantle, New York	42
1959	Ed Mathews, Milwaukee	46	Rocky Colavito, Cleveland	42
			Harmon Killebrew, Washington	
1960	Ernie Banks, Chicago	41	Mickey Mantle, New York	40
1961	Orlando Cepeda, San Francisco	46	Roger Maris, New York	61
1962	Willie Mays, San Francisco	49	Harmon Killebrew, Minnesota	48
1963	Hank Aaron, Milwaukee	44	Harmon Killebrew, Minnesota	45
	Willie McCovey, San Francisco			
1964	Willie Mays, San Francisco	47	Harmon Killebrew, Minnesota	49
1965	Willie Mays, San Francisco	52	Tony Conigliaro, Boston	32
1966	Hank Aaron, Atlanta	44	Frank Robinson, Baltimore	49
1967	Hank Aaron, Atlanta	39	Carl Yastrzemski, Boston	44
			Harmon Killebrew, Minnesota	
1968	Willie McCovey, San Francisco	36	Frank Howard, Washington	44
1969	Willie McCovey, San Francisco	45	Harmon Killebrew, Minnesota	49
1970	Johnny Bench, Cincinnati	45	Frank Howard, Washington	44
1971	Willie Stargell, Pittsburgh	48	Bill Melton, Chicago	33
1972	Johnny Bench, Cincinnati	40	Dick Allen, Chicago	37
1973	Willie Stargell, Pittsburgh	44	Reggie Jackson, Oakland	32
1974	Mike Schmidt, Philadelphia	36	Dick Allen, Chicago	32
1975	Mike Schmidt, Philadelphia	38	George Scott, Milwaukee	36
			Reggie Jackson, Oakland	
1976	Mike Schmidt, Philadelphia	38	Graig Nettles, New York	32
1977	George Foster, Cincinnati	52	Jim Rice, Boston	39
1978	George Foster, Cincinnati	40	Jim Rice, Boston	46
1979	Dave Kingman, Chicago	48	Gorman Thomas, Milwaukee	45
1980	Mike Schmidt, Philadelphia	48	Reggie Jackson, New York	41
			Ben Oglivie, Milwaukee	
1981	Mike Schmidt, Philadelphia	31	Bobby Grich, California	22
			Tony Armas, Oakland	
			Dwight Evans, Boston	
			Eddie Murray, Baltimore	
1982	Dave Kingman, New York	37	Gorman Thomas, Milwaukee	39
			Reggie Jackson, California	
1983	Mike Schmidt, Philadelphia	40	Jim Rice, Boston	39
1984	Mike Schmidt, Philadelphia	36	Tony Armas, Boston	43
	Dale Murphy, Atlanta			
1985	Dale Murphy, Atlanta	37	Darrell Evans, Detroit	40

Source: *The World Almanac and Book of Facts*, 1985 edition.

In which league does the leader tend to hit more home runs? To find out, we make the following back-to-back stem-and-leaf plot of these data. Notice that the stems are in the center of the plot.

NATIONAL LEAGUE		AMERICAN LEAGUE
9 8 8 8 7 3 3 1	2	2 2 4
9 9 8 8 8 7 7 7 6 6 6 6 5 4 4 3 3 1 1 1 1 0 0	3	2 2 2 2 2 2 2 3 3 3 4 5 6 6 6 7 7 7 7 9 9 9 9
9 9 8 8 8 7 7 7 7 6 6 5 5 4 4 4 4 3 3 3 2 2 1 1 0 0 0 0	4	0 0 1 1 1 2 2 2 3 3 3 3 4 4 4 4 5 5 6 6 6 6 6 7 8 8 9 9 9 9 9 9
6 4 2 2 1 1	5	2 4 8 8 9
	6	0 1

|2|4 REPRESENTS 24 HOME RUNS

There are too many leaves per stem, so we will spread out the stem-and-leaf plot using the stems that follow.

NATIONAL LEAGUE		AMERICAN LEAGUE
	2	
	·	
	3	
	·	
	4	
	·	
	5	
	·	
	6	

We will put the leaves 0, 1, 2, 3, and 4 on the first line for each stem and the leaves 5, 6, 7, 8, and 9 on the second line. The reorganized plot is shown as follows:

NATIONAL LEAGUE		AMERICAN LEAGUE
3 3 1	2	2 2 4
9 8 8 8 7	·	
4 4 3 3 1 1 1 1 0 0	3	2 2 2 2 2 2 3 3 3 4
9 9 8 8 8 7 7 6 6 6 5	·	5 6 6 6 7 7 7 7 9 9 9 9
4 4 4 4 3 3 3 2 2 1 1 0 0 0 0	4	0 0 1 1 1 2 2 2 3 3 3 4 4 4 4
9 9 8 8 8 7 7 7 7 6 6 5 5	·	5 5 6 6 6 6 7 8 8 9 9 9 9 9 9
4 2 2 1 1	5	2 4
6	·	8 8 9
	6	0 1

|2|4 REPRESENTS 24 HOME RUNS

Discussion Questions

1. Does the American League champion or the National League champion tend to hit the most home runs?

2. Which three years were unusually low in home runs hit in the American League? What happened in these three years?

3. Make a new back-to-back stem-and-leaf plot using the stems that follow. The home runs for the National League have been done for you. To construct this plot, you don't have to go back to the original list of data. Instead, take the values from one of the stem-and-leaf plots already constructed.

   For each stem, put the leaves:

   - 0 and 1 on the first line
   - 2 and 3 on the second line
   - 4 and 5 on the third line
   - 6 and 7 on the fourth line
   - 8 and 9 on the last line

```
       NATIONAL LEAGUE              |   |      AMERICAN LEAGUE
  _____  |   | _____
                              /  | 2 |
                          3  3  | . |
                                | . |
                              7 | . |
                      9  8  8 | . |
          /  /  /  /  0  0  | 3 |
                        3  3 | . |
                      5  4  4 | . |
        7  7  7  6  6  6  6 | . |
              9  9  8  8  8 | . |
          /  /  0  0  0  0  | 4 |
                3  3  3  2  2 | . |
            5  5  4  4  4  4 | . |
            7  7  7  7  6  6 | . |
              9  9  8  8  8 | . |
                        /  /  | 5 |
                        2  2 | . |
                           4 | . |
                           6 | . |
                             | . |
                             | 6 |
```

9|3| REPRESENTS
39 HOME RUNS

4. Which of the three back-to-back stem-and-leaf plots for the home run data do you think displays the data best? Why?

From a back-to-back plot like this, we can see that there tends to be a slightly larger number of home runs in the American League. We reach this conclusion because the values at the high end, in the upper 50's and 60's, come more often from the American League. Also, the values at the low end, in the 20's, come more often from the National League. For the stems in the 30's and the 40's, the numbers of leaves for the two leagues are about equal. The lower 50's has more values in the National League, but the American League makes up for this by having more values in the upper 50's and 60's.

Back-to-back stem-and-leaf plots are useful for comparing two sets of data. Before making comparisons, however, check to see first that both sets have about the same total number of values. Also, make sure that the plot is drawn accurately with each leaf taking up the same amount of space. These checks are important because we make the comparisons mainly through comparing the numbers of leaves on both sides. If one side has more data values or each leaf takes more space on one side than on the other, it can be hard to make accurate comparisons. To get the sizes correct, it helps to construct the plot on graph paper.

To decide if one data set generally has larger values than the other, compare the number of leaves on the two sides for both the largest and smallest stems. Also, note if there are outliers or gaps in the data that are not the same on both sides, and whether or not the two sides have about the same shape.

Application 6

Traffic Deaths

The table below lists the 50 states and the District of Columbia with the number of deaths in 1983 per 100 million vehicle miles driven.

Motor Vehicle Traffic Deaths by State
per 100 Million Vehicle Miles

Alabama	3.2	Montana	4.0
Alaska	3.9	Nebraska	2.1
Arizona	2.6	Nevada	3.8
Arkansas	3.2	New Hampshire	2.6
California	2.6	New Jersey	1.7
Colorado	2.6	New Mexico	4.3
Connecticut	2.1	New York	2.5
Delaware	2.3	North Carolina	2.8
District of Columbia	1.8	North Dakota	2.1
Florida	3.3	Ohio	2.1
Georgia	3.1	Oklahoma	2.7
Hawaii	2.2	Oregon	2.7
Idaho	3.2	Pennsylvania	2.4
Illinois	2.3	Rhode Island	1.6
Indiana	2.5	South Carolina	3.4
Iowa	2.5	South Dakota	2.6
Kansas	2.2	Tennessee	2.9
Kentucky	3.0	Texas	3.0
Louisiana	4.3	Utah	2.5
Maine	2.8	Vermont	2.3
Maryland	2.1	Virginia	2.1
Massachusetts	1.7	Washington	2.2
Michigan	2.1	West Virginia	4.4
Minnesota	1.8	Wisconsin	2.2
Mississippi	4.1	Wyoming	3.2
Missouri	2.5		

Source: National Safety Council.

1. If a state had 685 traffic deaths for 20,000,000,000 vehicle miles, what rate would be listed in the table above?

2. Alabama had a total of 940 auto deaths in 1983. How many miles were driven in Alabama that year?

3. How do the states east of the Mississippi River compare with the states west of it? To decide, construct a back-to-back stem-and-leaf plot with the stems spread out. You may want to use the map on page 15. Leave the values for Minnesota and Louisiana off the plot as the river goes through both states.

4. Which states east of the Mississippi River might be considered outliers?

5. Which state west of the Mississippi River has the highest traffic death rate? Would you call it an outlier?

6. Do states in the east or the west generally have larger traffic death rates?

7. Summarize what you learned from this back-to-back stem-and-leaf plot.

8. What factors do you think might help to explain the difference between the east and the west?

9. (For class discussion) How could these data have been collected?

Stem-and-Leaf Plots Where the Data Should be Truncated

The following table lists the buildings in San Francisco that are over 360 feet tall.

Building	Height in Feet
Transamerica Pyramid	853
Bank of America	778
101 California Street	600
5 Fremont Center	600
Embarcadero Center, Number 4	570
Security Pacific Bank	569
One Market Plaza, Spear Street	565
Wells Fargo Building	561
Standard Oil	551
One Sansome-Citicorp	550
Shaklee Building	537
Aetna Life	529
First & Market Building	529
Metropolitan Life	524
Crocker National Bank	500
Hilton Hotel	493
Pacific Gas & Electric	492
Union Bank	487
Pacific Insurance	476
Bechtel Building	475
333 Market Building	474
Hartford Building	465
Mutual Benefit Life	438
Russ Building	435
Pacific Telephone Building	435
Pacific Gateway	416
Embarcadero Center, Number 3	412
Embarcadero Center, Number 2	412
595 Market Building	410
101 Montgomery Street	405
California State Automobile Association	399
Alcoa Building	398
St. Francis Hotel	395
Shell Building	386
Del Monte	378
Pacific 3-Apparel Mart	376
Meridien Hotel	374

Source: *The World Almanac and Book of Facts*, 1985 edition.

The shortest building, the Meridien Hotel, is 374 feet tall. The tallest, the Transamerica Pyramid, is 853 feet tall. Start the stem-and-leaf plot as follows:

```
3
·
4
·
5
·
6
·
7
·
8
·
```

To place the 778-feet tall Bank of America Building on the plot, truncate (cut off) the last digit. This leaves 77, which goes on the plot as follows:

```
3
·
4
·
5
·
6
·
7
·   7
8
·
```

The finished plot follows.

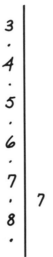

```
3
·   7 7 7 8 9 9 9
4   0 1 1 1 1 3 3 3
·   6 7 7 7 8 9 9
5   0 2 2 2 3
·   5 5 6 6 6 7
6   0 0
·
7
·   7
8
·   5
```

3|7 REPRESENTS
370 – 379 FEET

Discussion Questions

1. What heights can 8|5 represent?

2. The heights of all but two buildings stop abruptly at 600 feet. Can you think of a possible explanation for this?

3. The following table lists Los Angeles buildings taller than 360 feet.

Building	Height in Feet
First Interstate Bank	858
Crocker Center, North	750
Security Pacific National Bank	735
Atlantic Richfield Plaza (2 buildings)	699
Wells Fargo Bank	625
Crocker-Citizen Plaza	620
Century Plaza Towers (2 buildings)	571
Union Bank Square	516
City Hall	454
Equitable Life Building	454
Transamerica Center	452
Mutual Benefit Life Insurance Building	435
Broadway Plaza	414
1900 Avenue of Stars	398
1 Wilshire Building	395
The Evian	390
Bonaventure Hotel	367
400 South Hope Street	365
Beaudry Center	365
California Federal Savings & Loan Building	363
Century City Office Building	363

Source: *The World Almanac and Book of Facts*, 1985 edition.

Complete this back-to-back stem-and-leaf plot for the two cities.

LOS ANGELES		SAN FRANCISCO
	3	
	.	
	4	
	.	
	5	
	.	
	6	
	.	
	7	
	.	
	8	

Notice that San Francisco has 37 tall buildings, while Los Angeles has only 21. We don't need a stem-and-leaf plot to tell us that San Francisco has more tall buildings than Los Angeles. This plot can, however, help us answer the question of which city's buildings are relatively taller, apart from the total numbers of tall buildings. Unlike the last section, we cannot just look at the number of leaves, since San Francisco has more values and thus will generally have more leaves for each stem. Instead, we need to compare the two *shapes*, making a mental adjustment for the fact that San Francisco has about twice as many data values. Follow this procedure to answer the following question.

4. Considering only buildings over 360 feet tall, does Los Angeles or San Francisco tend to have relatively taller buildings?

5. In the previous stem-and-leaf plots, both the San Francisco and Los Angeles heights were truncated. Instead of truncating, we will now *round* each height to the nearest ten. Then we will see if the back-to-back stem-and-leaf plot gives the same impression as before. The San Francisco side of the plot below was made by rounding. Copy the plot and complete the Los Angeles side using rounding. The symbol 3|7 now represents 365-374 feet.

	LOS ANGELES			SAN FRANCISCO
		3		
		.	7 8 8 9	
		4	0 0 0 1 1 1 1 2 4 4 4	
		.	7 7 8 8 9 9 9	
		5	0 2 3 3 4	
		.	5 5 6 7 7 7	
		6	0 0	
		.		
		7		
		.	8	
		8		
		.	5	

3|7 REPRESENTS
365 - 374 FEET

6. Is it faster to round or to truncate?

7. Does the back-to-back stem-and-leaf plot with rounded numbers give the same general impression as the one with truncated numbers? Are there any differences in what you learn from the two plots?

8. Do you think truncating is an appropriate procedure, or should the data be rounded?

If you are like many students, you may feel that there is something wrong about truncating. It seems less accurate than rounding, and therefore worse. But is using 3|7 to represent 365-374 feet really more accurate for our purposes than using 3|7 to represent 370-379 feet?

Another point to consider is that the data we have may already be either rounded or truncated, and we don't know which. Are all the building heights exact multiples of one foot, with no inches or fractions of inches, as listed in the tables?

Finally, it is easy to make a mistake when rounding. In order to truncate, all we do is use a straightedge to cover the columns of digits not needed. To decide if truncating is appropriate for a specific problem, ask yourself if it is likely to make any difference in the interpretations you reach.

Children's Books

The following table lists the children's books published in the U.S. since 1895 that have sold one million or more copies.

Green Eggs and Ham, by Dr. Seuss. 1960	5,940,776
One Fish, Two Fish, Red Fish, Blue Fish, by Dr. Seuss. 1960	5,842,024
Hop on Pop, by Dr. Seuss. 1963	5,814,101
Dr. Seuss' ABC, by Dr. Seuss. 1963	5,648,193
The Cat in the Hat, by Dr. Seuss. 1957	5,394,741
The Wonderful Wizard of Oz, by L. Frank Baum. 1900	(estimate) 5,000,000
Charlotte's Web, by E. B. White. 1952	4,670,516
The Cat in the Hat Comes Back, by Dr. Seuss. 1958	3,431,917
The Little Prince, by Antoine de Saint-Exupery. 1943	2,811,478
The Little House on the Prairie, by Laura Ingalls Wilder. 1953 edition	2,732,666
The Little House in the Big Woods, by Laura Ingalls Wilder. 1953 edition	2,527,203
My First Atlas. 1959	2,431,000
Love and the Facts of Life, by Evelyn Duvall and Sylvanus Duvall. 1950	2,360,000
Egermeier's Bible Story Book, by Elsie E. Egermeier. 1923	2,326,577
Go Ask Alice, Anonymous. 1971	2,245,605
Benji, by Leonore Fleischer. 1974	2,235,694
The Little Engine That Could, by Watty Piper. 1926	2,166,000
Stuart Little, by E. B. White. 1945	2,129,591
Freckles, by Gene Stratton Potter. 1904	2,089,523
The Girl of the Limberlost, by Gene Stratton Porter. 1909	2,053,892
Sounder, by William Armstrong. 1969	1,815,401
Harry, the Dirty Dog, by Gene Zion. 1956	1,690,339
Seventeen, by Booth Tarkington. 1916	(estimate) 1,682,891
Where the Wild Things Are, by Maurice Sendak. 1963	1,632,020
Laddie, by Gene Stratton Porter. 1913	1,586,529
The Big Book of Mother Goose. 1950	1,500,000
The Golden Dictionary, by Ellen Wales Walpole. 1944	1,450,000
A Friend is Someone Who Likes You, by Joan Walsh Anglund. 1958	1,423,432
Rebecca of Sunnybrook Farm, by Kate Douglas Wiggin. 1904	1,357,714
Love Is a Special Way of Feeling, by Joan Walsh Anglund. 1960	1,308,293
The Real Mother Goose. 1915	1,296,140
The Pigman, by Paul Zindel. 1968	1,265,876
Better Homes and Gardens Story Book. 1951	1,220,728
Trouble after School, by Jerrold Beim. 1957	1,145,570
Better Homes and Gardens Junior Cook Book. 1955	1,100,182
Pollyanna, by Eleanor H. Porter. 1913	1,059,000
Le Petit Prince, by Antoine de Saint-Exupery. 1943	1,018,373
Mary Poppins, by Pamela L. Travers. 1934	1,005,203
Winnie-the Pooh, by A. A. Milne. 1926	1,005,000
Pollyanna Grows Up, by Eleanor H. Porter. 1915	1,000,000
Little Black Sambo, by Helen Bannerman. 1899	(estimate) 1,000,000

Source: A. P. Hackett and J. H. Burke, *Eighty Years of Best Sellers.*

1. Make a stem-and-leaf plot of these data using these stems. *Green Eggs and Ham* has been placed on the plot to get you started. Truncate all digits except those in the millions and hundred-thousands places.

```
1 |
  . |
2 |
  . |
3 |
  . |
4 |
  . |
5 |
  . | 9
```

1|0 REPRESENTS 1,000,000 THROUGH 1,099,999 BOOKS SOLD

2. Underline all digits representing books by Dr. Seuss.

3. Circle the digits representing the books you have read. Do these circles tend to be at the top or the bottom of the diagram? Why?

4. If another line were added to the top of the plot for books that sold 500,000-999,999 copies, how long do you think it would be? Why?

5. Write a summary of the information displayed in the plot.

Stem-and-Leaf Plots — Summary

Stem-and-leaf plots are a new way to quickly organize and display data. Unlike line plots, they are best used when there are more than 25 pieces of data. Statisticians use stem-and-leaf plots as a substitute for the less informative histograms and bar graphs.

Variations of stem-and-leaf plots that you should know how to construct are as follows:

- back-to-back

- truncated and rounded

- spread out

From a stem-and-leaf plot it is easy to identify the largest and smallest values, outliers, clusters, gaps, the relative position of any important value, and the shape of the distribution.

Suggestions for Student Projects

1. Collect data on a topic that interests you, make a stem-and-leaf plot, and then write a summary of the information displayed in the plot. Use one of the topics listed below or think of your own.

    a. Compare the ages in months of the boys and the girls in your class.

    b. Compare the heights of the boys and the girls in your class.

    c. Compare the heights of the buildings in two cities near you.

    d. Compare the gas mileage of foreign and domestic cars. (This information can be found in many almanacs.)

    e. Compare the scores of two different classes taking the same math test.

    The next two projects involve comparing line plots with stem-and-leaf plots.

2. Devise a way to use symbols in a line plot to replace the individual data values, as we did for the stem-and-leaf plots in the fast foods and thunderstorm examples. Then, construct a line plot for one of these examples, using your method. Do the line and stem-and-leaf plots show any different information? Which is easier to interpret? Which do you prefer?

3. Devise a way of modifying a line plot to get a back-to-back line plot. Then, redo Application 6, or the building heights example, using your back-to-back line plot. Which is easier to construct, the back-to-back line plot or the stem-and-leaf plot? Do they show any different information? Which shows the information more clearly? Which do you prefer? Can you think of situations in which you might prefer the other plot?

4. In order to compare truncating and rounding, take any of the data in this section and make a back-to-back stem-and-leaf plot of the truncated against the rounded values. Do you see any difference, and if so what is it? Could you have predicted this?

5. In the fast foods example at the beginning of this section, we showed the type of food in the stem-and-leaf plot by replacing the leaves by letters. A way to show both the specific numerical values and labels is to keep the numerical leaf in the plot, and follow it by a label in parentheses. For instance, the next-to-bottom row in the fast foods example would be 3|3(H), 4(F). By keeping the number in the plot, we retain as much detailed numerical information as is generally needed. This idea is especially useful for displaying data where there is one number for each of the 50 states. The two-letter postal abbreviation can be used to identify each state. Find some interesting data where there is one value for each state. A good example would be each state's current population as found in an almanac. Make the plot just described, and write a summary of the information displayed.

III. MEDIAN, MEAN, QUARTILES, AND OUTLIERS

Median and Mean

You have probably learned how to compute the average of a set of numbers. For example, if Sally gets scores of 80, 96, 84, 95, and 90 on five math tests, then her average is:

$$\frac{80 + 96 + 84 + 95 + 90}{5}$$

$$= \frac{445}{5}$$

$$= 89.$$

Whenever we compute an average this way, we will call it the *mean*. Thus, the mean of Sally's test scores is 89. We need a new word for the average because there are other kinds of averages. Another type of average is the *median*. To find the median of Sally's test scores, first put them in order from smallest to largest.

$$80 \quad 84 \quad \boxed{90} \quad 95 \quad 96$$

The middle score, 90, is the median. Half of Sally's five test scores are lower than or equal to the median and half are higher than or equal to the median.

What do you do if there is an even number of scores? If Sally takes a sixth test and gets a 25, her scores are now:

$$25 \quad 80 \quad \boxed{84 \quad 90} \quad 95 \quad 96.$$

There are two scores in the middle, 84 and 90. The median is halfway between these two scores:

$$\frac{84 + 90}{2}$$

$$= \frac{174}{2}$$

$$= 87.$$

Half of her six test scores are lower than 87 and half are higher.

Discussion Questions

1. Compute the mean of Sally's six test scores. (Round to the nearest tenth.)

2. On the basis of this grading scale what grade would Sally receive if the mean of the six tests is used to determine her grade?

   A 90-100   B 80-89   C 70-79   D 60-69   E 0-59

3. What grade would she receive if the median of the six tests is used to determine her grade?

4. Does one extreme score cause a greater change in the median or in the mean?

5. Do you need to know all of the data values in order to find the median? For example, suppose that Sally has taken 6 tests and you only know 5 of her scores. Can you calculate the median?

6. Give a reason for choosing the median to summarize Sally's test scores.

7. Give a reason for choosing the mean to summarize Sally's test scores.

8. Which do you think is better to use, the mean or median?

9. Why do you think the median is generally used when discussing ages, average house prices, or average incomes, as in the following newspaper and magazine examples?

   a. "When only first-time marriages were considered, the agency [National Center for Health Statistics] placed the median age for brides at 21.8 years in 1980, up from 20.3 years in 1963. The median age for bridegrooms was 23.6 years, up from 22.5 years in 1963." (Los Angeles Times 2/17/84)

   b. According to the Census Bureau, "the counties with the highest median value of owner-occupied dwellings are: Pitkin, CO. - $200,000; Marin, CA - $151,000; Honolulu, HI - $130,400; San Mateo, CA - $124,400; Maui, HI - $113,600." (USA Today 3/8/84)

   c. According to the Census Bureau, "the median time spent on homework for students in American elementary and high schools was 5.4 hours a week . . . the sharpest difference was between types of schools, with students in private high schools doing 14.2 hours of homework weekly, as against 6.5 hours by their public school counterparts." (The New York Times 11/29/84)

   d. "The following drawing shows typical allowances (rounded to the nearest 25¢) for 8-to-13-year-olds, as reported by the 811 students in our survey who received allowances. The allowances of the 8-to-11-year-olds are all pretty much the same. They range from $2.00 to $2.75. But for the 12-year-olds, there's a jump of $1, and an even bigger jump for kids one year older.

   The figures don't mean that all the three hundred thirty-eight 11-year-olds in our survey who receive an allowance are pocketing $2.75 every week. That $2.75 is the *median* allowance for that age. Median means right in the middle. Half the 11-year-olds are getting more than $2.75, and half are getting less. In fact, one-third report a weekly allowance of under $2, and about the same amount get more than $4 a week.

169 get less	$2.75	169 get more

   The amount of your allowance seems to depend a lot on your age. But where you live and whether you are a boy or a girl do *not* seem to affect how much you get per week. Students all across the country, in cities and small towns, said they received pretty much the same amount. Boys and girls also reported similar allowances." *(Penny Power 2/3/83)*

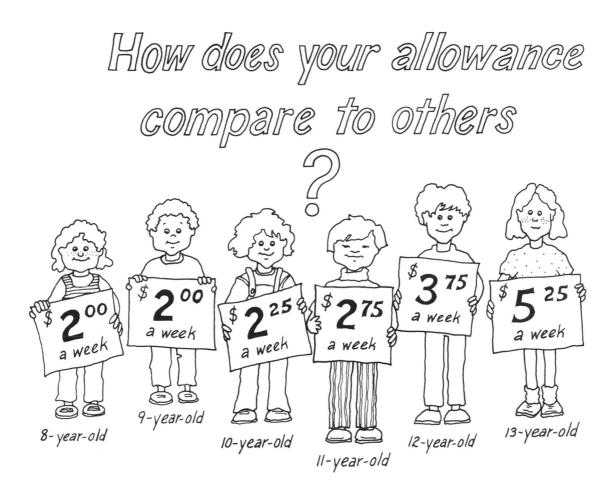

10. In the following newspaper story, what do you think is the meaning of the word "average"? Give your reasons.

"[In a study of jury awards in civil trials, they] found that while the average award against corporate defendants was more than $120,000, the average against individuals was $18,500. The average against government defendants was $38,000, but it was $97,000 in cases that involved hospitals and other nonprofit entities.

'To some degree, the average awards against corporations and hospitals were so great because of a few extraordinarily large awards,' the report explained." *(Newark Star-Ledger 8/20/85)*

11. The following information seems to be incorrect.

"According to the latest enrollment analysis by age-categories, half of the [Los Angeles Community College] district's 128,000 students are over the age of 24. The average student is 29." *(Los Angeles Times 9/20/81)*

"In the region we are traveling west of Whitney, precipitation drops off and the average snow depth on April 1 for the southern Sierra is a modest 5 to 6 feet. And two winters out of three, the snow pack is below average." Ezra Bowen, *The High Sierra* (New York: Time-Life Books, 1972), p. 142.

a. Give an example of four students with a mean age of 29 and median age of 24.

b. Give an example of the snow depth for three winters that makes the quote from *The High Sierra* true.

Both the median and the mean summarize the data by giving a measure of the center of the data values. *For the kinds of data in this book*, the median generally gives a more reasonable summary since it is not affected by a few extreme values. When there are no outliers, there will generally not be much difference between the median and mean, and which we choose won't matter. Using a calculator, the mean is easy to compute. To find the median, however, the data must be ordered from smallest to largest. This can be tedious, but an easy method is to construct a stem-and-leaf plot.

Neither the median nor the mean can tell us as much about the data as a plot showing all the values, such as a line plot or a stem-and-leaf plot.

Application 8

How Many Moons?

A visitor from the star Alpha Centauri has selected you to provide her with information about our solar system. She is filling out a form and asks how many moons are "average" for a planet in our solar system.

Study the table below.

Planet	Number of Moons
Mercury	0
Venus	0
Earth	1
Mars	2
Jupiter	16
Saturn	23
Uranus	15*
Neptune	2
Pluto	1

Source: The World Book, 1984.
*The published figure is 5 moons, but in January 1986, Voyager 2
discovered 10 additional moons around Uranus.

1. Compute the mean number of moons.

2. Compute the median number of moons.

3. Which three planets are the most different in number of moons compared to the others? Do you know any explanation for this?

4. Do you think the visitor from Alpha Centauri would get a more accurate impression about the typical number of moons from the median or the mean? Is either summary number adequate? Give your reasons.

   Next, the visitor asks about the length of a typical day in our solar system. Study the following table.

Planet	Approximate Length of a Day in Earth Hours
Mercury	1416
Venus	5832
Earth	24
Mars	24.5
Jupiter	10
Saturn	11
Uranus	22
Neptune	16
Pluto	153

5. Compute the mean length of a day in our solar system in hours.

6. How many Earth days is this?

7. Find the median length of a day in our solar system.

8. Do you think it is better to give your visitor the mean length of a day or the median length of a day? Why? Are you happy about giving your visitor one single number? Why or why not?

Application 9

The Pop Meter

Six of the pop music reviewers for the *Los Angeles Times* and a teenage actress and singer, Molly Ringwald, rated five new albums as follows:

Albums	Dennis Hunt	Lori E. Pike	Richard Cromelin	Connie Johnson	Chris Willman	Patrick Goldstein	Molly Ringwald
"Little Creatures" Talking Heads	75	84	85	75	88	91	95
"Who's Zoomin' Who?" Aretha Franklin	86	82	70	83	62	79	98
"Youthquake" Dead or Alive	78	72	50	30	12	36	70
"Boy in the Box" Corey Hart	60	60	20	49	25	51	75
"Invasion of Your Privacy" Ratt	65	20	20	25	27	66	90

The ratings system: 90-100, excellent; 70-89, good; 50-69, fair; 30-49, weak; 0-29, melt down.

Source: *Los Angeles Times*, September 1, 1985.

1. Compute the mean rating for each album.

2. Compute the median rating for each album.

3. a) For which album are the mean and median farthest apart?

   b) Which reviewer caused this?

   c) Is the mean or the median more representative of this album's overall rating?

4. a) If you judge by the mean rating, which reviewer is the hardest grader?

   b) If you judge by the median rating, which reviewer is the hardest grader?

   c) Which reviewer tends to be the most different from the others?

Range, Quartiles, and Interquartile Range

The number of grams of carbohydrates (starch and sugar) in a 1-ounce serving of thirteen breakfast cereals is shown below.

Cereal	Carbohydrates	Cereal	Carbohydrates
Life	19	Grape Nuts	23
Super Sugar Crisp	26	Special K	21
Rice Krispies	25	Raisin Bran	28
Product 19	24	Wheaties	23
Total	23	Puffed Rice	13
Sugar Corn Pops	26	Sugar Smacks	25
		Cheerios	20

To find the *range*, subtract the smallest number from the largest. The range for the carbohydrates is:

$$28 - 13 = 15 \text{ grams.}$$

We will also learn how to find the *lower quartile* and the *upper quartile*. If the numbers are arranged in order from smallest to largest, the lower quartile, the median, and the upper quartile divide them into four groups of roughly the same size.

X X X X X X X X X X X X X X X X X X X X X X X X X X

| LOWER | LOWER | MEDIAN | UPPER | UPPER |
| EXTREME | QUARTILE | | QUARTILE | EXTREME |

To find the quartiles of the previous numbers, first arrange the numbers in order:

13   19   20   21   23   23   23   24   25   25   26   26   28

Second, find the median and draw a vertical line through it.

13   19   20   21   23   23   23   24   25   25   26   26   28

The median is 23. Six numbers are below this 23 and six are above it.

Third, consider only the data values to the left of the line.

13   19   20 | 21   23   23

The median of these six numbers is between 20 and 21. This is the lower quartile. Thus, the lower quartile is 20.5. We have drawn a vertical line at the median of these values in the same way as before.

Finally, consider only the data values to the right of the line and find their median. This is the upper quartile. The upper quartile is 25.5.

$$24 \quad 25 \quad 25 \mid 26 \quad 26 \quad 28$$

We have divided the numbers into four groups:

$$13 \quad 19 \quad 20 \mid 21 \quad 23 \quad 23 \quad 23 \quad 24 \quad 25 \quad 25 \mid 26 \quad 26 \quad 28$$

Notice that there are three numbers in each group.

The *interquartile range* is the difference between the upper quartile and the lower quartile. The interquartile range of the given numbers is:

$$25.5 - 20.5 = 5.$$

The *lower extreme* is the smallest value in the data. In this case, it is 13. Similarly, the *upper extreme* is the largest number in the data. In this case, it is 28.

The fastest way to order the numbers from smallest to largest is to make a stem-and-leaf plot of the data, with the leaves ordered. Then, count in from the top and bottom to mark the median and quartiles. As an example, suppose we did not have Cheerios in the list of cereals and we wanted the median and quartiles of the remaining 12 cereals. The median will then be between the sixth and seventh values. We draw the first line there and consider only the data values below and above this line, as before, to get the quartiles.

```
1 | 3
· | 9
2 | 1 | 3  3  3 | 4
· | 5  5 | 6  6 | 8
```

The vertical lines here are dotted. The median is 23.5, the lower quartile is 22, and the upper quartile is 25.5.

Discussion Questions

1. In these data, the median is the mean of the quartiles. Will the median always be the mean of the quartiles?

2. Is the interquartile range half of the range?

3. Cross the 13 grams from Puffed Rice off the list and find the new median and quartiles.

4. By how much did these values change?

5. Recompute the range and interquartile range.

6. By how much did these values change?

7. Find two different sets of seven numbers with:

   lower extreme - 3
   lower quartile - 5
   median - 10
   upper quartile - 12
   upper extreme - 13

8. The median is always between the two quartiles. Do you think the *mean* is always between the two quartiles?

9. Find a set of seven numbers where the mean is above the upper quartile.

10. Find a set of seven numbers where the mean is below the lower quartile.

Application 10

Motocross Bike Ratings

The list below contains the ratings by *Penny Power* magazine of 22 motocross bikes.

Rating	Brand	Model	Price
Very Good	Raleigh	R-10 TUFF BMF	$190
Very Good	Raleigh	R-10 MK III	$150
Very Good	Schwinn	B43 Scrambler	$196
Very Good	Mongoose	BMX Wirewheel	$190
Very Good	Mongoose	BMX Freemag	$215
Good	Vista	GTX99	$125
Good	J.C.Penney	Eagle V	$190
Fair	Ross	142-25 THX	$165
Fair	Ross	Slinger	$125
Fair	Sears	Free Spirit BMX FS500	$150
Fair	Schwinn	B511 Thrasher	$143
Fair	Sears	BMX FS100	$100
Fair	Murray	X-20 Team Murray	$141
Fair	AMF	Hawk 4 BMX	$139
Fair	Huffy	Pro Thunder BMX	$160
Fair	Columbia	Pro Am 2236	$160
Poor	Murray	Team Murray BMX	$130
Poor	J.C.Penney	Dirt Tracker II	$110
Poor	Wards	BMX 34 Open Road	$80
Poor	AMF	Avenger Motocross	$100
Poor	Columbia	Formula 16 BMX	$110
Poor	Huffy	Thunder BMX	$100

Source: *Penny Power*, February 3, 1983.

1. What is the most expensive bike?
2. What is the least expensive bike?

3. Find the median price of the bikes rated:

    a. very good

    b. good

    c. fair

    d. poor

4. In general, do bikes with a higher price have a higher rating?

5. What is the range of the bike prices?

6. Find the lower quartile for all bikes.

7. Find the upper quartile.

8. What is the interquartile range of the bike prices?

9. Which of the bikes rated "very good" is priced below the upper quartile? Is this bike a good buy?

10. Which of the bikes rated "poor" is priced above the lower quartile? Is this bike a good buy?

Outliers

The following table lists all 15 records that reached number 1 for the first time in 1959, and the total number of weeks that each record held the number 1 spot.

Weeks	Record Title	Artist
3	"Smoke Gets in Your Eyes"	Platters
4	"Stagger Lee"	Lloyd Price
5	"Venus"	Frankie Avalon
4	"Come Softly to Me"	Fleetwoods
1	"The Happy Organ"	Dave 'Baby' Cortez
2	"Kansas City"	Wilbert Harrison
6	"The Battle of New Orleans"	Johnny Horton
4	"Lonely Boy"	Paul Anka
2	"A Big Hunk o' Love"	Elvis Presley
4	"The Three Bells"	Browns
2	"Sleep Walk"	Santo & Johnny
9	"Mack the Knife"	Bobby Darin
1	"Mr. Blue"	Fleetwoods
2	"Heartaches by the Number"	Guy Mitchell
1	"Why"	Frankie Avalon

Source: *The Billboard Book of Top 40 Hits*, 1985.

We have already used the word *outlier* several times to indicate values that are widely separated from the rest of the data. Would you say that any record in the list above is an outlier? If we think we have spotted an outlier, it is worth some special thought about why it is different from the rest. Trying to make sense out of the outliers can be an important part of interpreting data.

It is not reasonable, however, to automatically call the upper and lower extremes outliers. Any data set has extremes, and we don't want to put extra energy into trying to interpret them unless they are separated from the rest of the data. We could decide if an observation is an outlier by looking at a plot and making a decision, as we have done so far. However, it is helpful to have a rule to aid in making the decision, especially when there are a moderate to large number of observations (say 25 or more).

Thus, we say that an *outlier* is any number more than 1.5 interquartile ranges above the upper quartile, or more than 1.5 interquartile ranges below the lower quartile. A line plot of the hit record data, with the median (M) and quartiles (LQ and UQ) labeled, follows.

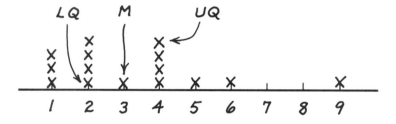

The interquartile range (IQR) is $4 - 2 = 2$, so $1.5 \times IQR = 3$. Thus, the upper cut-off is $4 + 3 = 7$. Since the data value 9 ("Mack the Knife") is greater than 7, we call it an outlier. For the lower end, the cut-off is $2 - 3 = -1$. Since no data value can be less than -1, there are no outliers at the lower end. An interpretation we can draw is that "Mack the Knife" was not only the most popular record in 1959, but that it really stands out as substantially more popular than the other 14 top hits. Before doing this calculation, did you feel that "Mack the Knife" was an outlier?

The rule just described is quick, easy, and straightforward to use. Multiplying the IQR by 1.5 rather than 1.0 or 2.0 generally produces results that are what we would like, if we were to decide which values should be labeled outliers. You might experiment using multipliers such as 1.0, 1.5, and 2.0 to decide which you prefer.

Ice Cream Cone Prices

In September 1985, the prices of a single–scoop ice cream cone at 17 Los Angeles stores are given in the table below.

Store (brand)	Price
Andi's (homemade)	$ .90
Baskin-Robbins	.75
Carvel	.95
Cecelia's (Dreyers)	.90
Cinema Sweet (homemade)	1.20
Clancy Muldoon	.95
Creamery (homemade)	1.05
Farrell's	.70
Foster's Freeze	.53
Haagen-Dazs	1.10
Humphrey Yogart	.95
Leatherby's (homemade)	.91
Magic Sundae (Buds)	.96
Robb's (homemade)	.95
Swensons	1.00
Thrifty Drug	.25
Will-Wright's (own recipe)	1.15

1. Make a stem-and-leaf plot of the prices.

2. Are there any gaps in the prices? Where?

3. Find the median price of an ice cream cone using the stem-and-leaf plot.

4. Find the mean price of an ice cream cone.

5. Thrifty Drug's cone is much cheaper than the others. If it is taken off the list, do you think the median or the mean will increase the most?

6. Cross Thrifty Drug's price off the list before determining the following:

   a. Find the median price of the remaining cones.

   b. Find the mean price of the remaining cones.

   c. Which increased more, the median or the mean?

7. Find the range in prices. (Include Thrifty Drug from exercise 7 through 13).

8. Find the lower quartile of the prices.

9. Find the upper quartile of the prices.

10. Is there a larger difference between the median and the lower quartile or between the median and the upper quartile?

11. Find the interquartile range.

12. Use the 1.5 × IQR rule to find any outliers.

13. How is the outlier different from the others? Can you think of any possible explanations for this?

Median, Mean, Quartiles, and Outliers — Summary

Both the median and the mean are single numbers that summarize the location of the data. Neither alone can tell the whole story about the data, but sometimes we do want a single, concise, summary value. Generally, the median is more valuable than the mean, especially if there is any possibility of having even a few unusually large or small values in the data.

The lower quartile, median, and upper quartile divide the data into four parts with approximately the same number of observations in each part. The interquartile range (IQR), the third quartile minus the first quartile, is a measure of how spread out the data are. If a number is more than 1.5 times the interquartile range above the upper quartile or below the lower quartile, we call it an outlier. If the data are grouped fairly tightly, there will be no outliers. When we do find an outlier, we should study it closely. It is worthwhile to try to find reasons for it, as they can be an important part of the overall interpretation of the data.

Suggestions for Student Projects

1. Choose 5 or 6 current popular records. Your teacher should select 5 or 6 reviewers from students in your class. These reviewers will fill in ratings as in Application 9, and the entire class will analyze the results.

2. Find examples of the use of the words "mean," "median," or "average" in a local newspaper. If you find "average," can you tell if they used the median, the mean, or some other method? If you find "mean" or "median," discuss whether or not the appropriate method was used.

3. The following data give the Number 1 hit records in each of 10 years. The class will work in groups. Each group takes the data from one year, makes a line plot, and identifies outliers using several different rules (for example, multipliers of 1.0, 1.5, and 2.0, or other appropriate multipliers). Then, each group decides which rule it likes the best for its data. Finally, discuss the results among the whole class. What is your choice?

1960

Weeks	Record Title	Artist
2	El Paso	Marty Robbins
3	Running Bear	Johnny Preston
2	Teen Angel	Mark Dinning
9	Theme from 'A Summer Place'	Percy Faith
4	Stuck on You	Elvis Presley
5	Cathy's Clown	Everly Brothers
2	Everybody's Somebody's Fool	Connie Francis
1	Alley-Oop	Hollywood Argyles
3	I'm Sorry	Brenda Lee
1	Itsy Bitsy Teeny Weeny Yellow Polkadot Bikini	Brian Hyland
5	It's Now or Never	Elvis Presley
1	The Twist	Chubby Checker
2	My Heart Has a Mind of Its Own	Connie Francis
1	Mr. Custer	Larry Verne
3	Save the Last Dance for Me	Drifters
1	I Want to Be Wanted	Brenda Lee
1	Georgia on My Mind	Ray Charles
1	Stay	Maurice Williams & The Zodiacs
6	Are You Lonesome Tonight?	Elvis Presley

Source: *The Billboard Book of Top 40 Hits*, 1985.

1962

Weeks	Record Title	Artist
2	The Twist	Chubby Checker
3	Peppermint Twist	Joey Dee & The Starliters
3	Duke of Earl	Gene Chandler
3	Hey! Baby	Bruce Channel
1	Don't Break the Heart That Loves You	Connie Francis
2	Johnny Angel	Shelley Fabares
2	Good Luck Charm	Elvis Presley
3	Soldier Boy	Shirelles
1	Stranger on the Shore	Mr. Acker Bilk
5	I Can't Stop Loving You	Ray Charles
1	The Stripper	David Rose
4	Roses Are Red	Bobby Vinton
2	Breaking Up Is Hard to Do	Neil Sedaka
1	The Loco-Motion	Little Eva
2	Sheila	Tommy Roe
5	Sherry	4 Seasons
2	Monster Mash	Boris Pickett & The Crypt Kickers
2	He's A Rebel	Crystals
5	Big Girls Don't Cry	4 Seasons
3	Telstar	Tornadoes

Source: *The Billboard Book of Top 40 Hits*, 1985.

1964

Weeks	Record Title	Artist
4	There! I've Said It Again	Bobby Vinton
7	I Want to Hold Your Hand	Beatles
2	She Loves You	Beatles
5	Can't Buy Me Love	Beatles
1	Hello, Dolly!	Louis Armstrong
2	My Guy	Mary Wells
1	Love Me Do	Beatles
3	Chapel of Love	Dixie Cups
1	A World Without Love	Peter & Gordon
2	I Get Around	Beach Boys
2	Rag Doll	4 Seasons
2	A Hard Day's Night	Beatles
1	Everybody Loves Somebody	Dean Martin
2	Where Did Our Love Go?	Supremes
3	The House of the Rising Sun	Animals
3	Oh, Pretty Woman	Roy Orbison
2	Do Wah Diddy Diddy	Manfred Mann
4	Baby Love	Supremes
1	Leader of the Pack	Shangri-Las
1	Ringo	Lorne Greene
1	Mr. Lonely	Bobby Vinton
2	Come See About Me	Supremes
3	I Feel Fine	Beatles

Source: *The Billboard Book of Top 40 Hits,* 1985.

1966

Weeks	Record Title	Artist
2	The Sounds of Silence	Simon & Garfunkle
3	We Can Work It Out	Beatles
2	My Love	Petula Clark
1	Lightnin' Strikes	Lou Christie
1	These Boots Are Made for Walkin'	Nancy Sinatra
5	The Ballad of the Green Berets	Sgt. Barry Sadler
3	(You're My) Soul and Inspiration	Righteous Brothers
1	Good Lovin'	Young Rascals
3	Monday, Monday	Mamas & Papas
2	When a Man Loves a Woman	Percy Sledge
2	Paint It Black	Rolling Stones
2	Paperback Writer	Beatles
1	Strangers in the Night	Frank Sinatra
2	Hanky Panky	Tommy James & The Shondells
2	Wild Thing	Troggs
3	Summer in the City	Lovin' Spoonful
1	Sunshine Superman	Donovan
2	You Can't Hurry Love	Supremes
3	Cherish	Association
2	Reach Out I'll Be There	Four Tops
1	96 Tears	? & The Mysterians
1	Last Train to Clarksville	Monkees
1	Poor Side of Town	Johnny Rivers
2	You Keep Me Hangin' On	Supremes
3	Winchester Cathedral	New Vaudeville Band
1	Good Vibrations	Beach Boys
7	I'm a Believer	Monkees

Source: *The Billboard Book of Top 40 Hits,* 1985.

1968

Weeks	Record Title	Artist
2	Judy in Disguise (With Glasses)	John Fred & His Playboy Band
1	Green Tambourine	Lemon Pipers
5	Love Is Blue	Paul Mauriat
4	(Sittin' on) The Dock of the Bay	Otis Redding
5	Honey	Bobby Goldsboro
2	Tighten Up	Archie Bell & The Drells
3	Mrs. Robinson	Simon & Garfunkel
4	This Guy's in Love with You	Herb Alpert
2	Grazing in the Grass	Hugh Masekela
2	Hello, I Love You	Doors
5	People Got to Be Free	Rascals
1	Harper Valley P.T.A.	Jeannie C. Riley
9	Hey Jude	Beatles
2	Love Child	Diana Ross & The Supremes
7	I Heard It Through the Grapevine	Marvin Gaye

Source: *The Billboard Book of Top 40 Hits*, 1985.

1980

Weeks	Record Title	Artist
1	Please Don't Go	KC & The Sunshine Band
4	Rock with You	Michael Jackson
1	Do That to Me One More Time	Captain & Tenille
4	Crazy Little Thing Called Love	Queen
4	Another Brick in the Wall (Part II)	Pink Floyd
6	Call Me	Blondie
4	Funkytown	Lipps, Inc.
3	Coming Up (Live at Glasgow)	Paul McCartney & Wings
2	It's Still Rock and Roll to Me	Billy Joel
4	Magic	Olivia Newton-John
1	Sailing	Christopher Cross
4	Upside Down	Diana Ross
3	Another One Bites the Dust	Queen
3	Woman In Love	Barbra Streisand
6	Lady	Kenny Rogers
5	(Just Like) Starting Over	John Lennon

Source: *The Billboard Book of Top 40 Hits*, 1985.

1981

Weeks	Record Title	Artist
1	The Tide Is High	Blondie
2	Celebration	Kool & The Gang
2	9 to 5	Dolly Parton
2	I Love a Rainy Night	Eddie Rabbitt
1	Keep on Loving You	REO Speedwagon
2	Rapture	Blondie
3	Kiss on My List	Daryl Hall & John Oates
2	Morning Train (Nine to Five)	Sheena Easton
9	Bette Davis Eyes	Kim Carnes
1	Stars on 45 Medley	Stars on 45
1	The One That You Love	Air Supply
2	Jessie's Girl	Rick Springfield
9	Endless Love	Diana Ross & Lionel Richie
3	Arthur's Theme (Best That You Can Do)	Christopher Cross
2	Private Eyes	Daryl Hall & John Oates
10	Physical	Olivia Newton-John

Source: *The Billboard Book of Top 40 Hits*, 1985.

1982

Weeks	Record Title	Artist
1	I Can't Go for That (No Can Do)	Daryl Hall & John Oates
6	Centerfold	J. Geils Band
7	I Love Rock 'n Roll	Joan Jett & The Blackhearts
1	Chariots of Fire	Vangelis
7	Ebony and Ivory	Paul McCartney/Stevie Wonder
3	Don't You Want Me	Human League
6	Eye of the Tiger	Survivor
2	Abracadabra	Steve Miller Band
2	Hard to Say I'm Sorry	Chicago
4	Jack & Diane	John Cougar
1	Who Can It Be Now?	Men at Work
3	Up Where We Belong	Joe Cocker & Jennifer Warnes
2	Truly	Lionel Richie
1	Mickey	Toni Basil
4	Maneater	Daryl Hall & Joan Oates

Source: *The Billboard Book of Top 40 Hits*, 1985.

1983

Weeks	Record Title	Artist
4	Down Under	Men at Work
1	Africa	Toto
2	Baby, Come to Me	Patti Austin & James Ingram
7	Billie Jean	Michael Jackson
1	Come On Eileen	Dexys Midnight Runners
3	Beat It	Michael Jackson
1	Let's Dance	David Bowie
6	Flashdance...What a Feeling	Irene Cara
8	Every Breath You Take	Police
1	Sweet Dreams (Are Made of This)	Eurythmics
2	Maniac	Michael Sembello
1	Tell Her About It	Billy Joel
4	Total Eclipse of the Heart	Bonnie Tyler
2	Islands in the Stream	Kenny Rogers with Dolly Parton
4	All Night Long (All Night)	Lionel Richie
6	Say Say Say	Paul McCartney & Michael Jackson

Source: *The Billboard Book of Top 40 Hits,* 1985.

1984

Weeks	Record Title	Artist
2	Owner of a Lonely Heart	Yes
3	Karma Chameleon	Culture Club
5	Jump	Van Halen
3	Footloose	Kenny Loggins
3	Against All Odds (Take a Look at Me Now)	Phil Collins
2	Hello	Lionel Richie
2	Let's Hear It for the Boy	Deniece Williams
2	Time After Time	Cyndi Lauper
2	The Reflex	Duran Duran
5	When Doves Cry	Prince
3	Ghostbusters	Ray Parker, Jr.
3	What's Love Got to Do with It?	Tina Turner
1	Missing You	John Waite
2	Let's Go Crazy	Prince
3	I Just Called to Say I Love You	Stevie Wonder
2	Caribbean Queen (No More Love on the Run)	Billy Ocean
3	Wake Me Up Before You Go-Go	WHAM!
2	Out of Touch	Daryl Hall & John Oates
6	Like a Virgin	Madonna

Source: *The Billboard Book of Top 40 Hits,* 1985.

IV. BOX PLOTS

In the last section, we learned how to find the extremes, the quartiles and the median. These five numbers tell us a great deal about a set of data. In this section, we will describe a way of using them to make a plot.

The following tables give the ratings for national prime-time television for the week of April 29 through May 5, 1985, as compiled by the A. C. Nielsen Co. The 25.5 rating for *The Cosby Show* means that out of every 100 houses with televisions, 25.5 were watching *The Cosby Show* at the time it was on. Each ratings point represents 849,000 TV households.

TELEVISION RATINGS

	Program	Network	Rating
1.	The Cosby Show	NBC	25.5
2.	Family Ties	NBC	21.9
3.	Dallas	CBS	21.4
4.	Cheers	NBC	19.7
5.	Newhart	CBS	18.4
6.	Falcon Crest	CBS	18.3
7.	"Alfred Hitchcock Presents"	NBC	18.0
8.	60 Minutes	CBS	17.9
9.	Knots Landing	CBS	17.8
10.	A-Team	NBC	17.6
11.	Murder, She Wrote	CBS	17.6
12.	Night Court	NBC	17.6
13.	Highway to Heaven	NBC	17.0
14.	Facts of Life	NBC	16.8
15.	"Missing, Have You Seen This Person?"	NBC	16.5
16.	Kate & Allie	CBS	16.3
17.	Sara	NBC	16.3
18.	Who's the Boss?	ABC	15.9
19.	Trapper John, M.D.	CBS	15.7
20.	Love Boat	ABC	15.5
21.	Scarecrow & Mrs. King	CBS	15.4
22.	"Miss Hollywood '85"	ABC	15.4
23.	"Lace II," Part I	ABC	15.3
24.	Miami Vice	NBC	15.2
25.	Simon & Simon	CBS	15.2
26.	Riptide	NBC	15.2
27.	Cagney & Lacey	CBS	15.0
28.	"Adam"	NBC	14.9
29.	Crazy Like a Fox	CBS	14.6
30.	MacGruder and Loud	ABC	14.3
31.	20/20	ABC	14.3
32.	"Life's Embarrassing Moments"	ABC	14.2
33.	Hill Street Blues	NBC	14.0

Source: A.C. Nielsen Company.

TELEVISION RATINGS

	Program	Network	Rating
34.	St. Elsewhere	NBC	13.9
35.	Three's a Crowd	ABC	13.8
36.	Hail to the Chief	ABC	13.7
37.	"Joanna"	ABC	13.0
38.	Airwolf	CBS	12.7
39.	Remington Steele	NBC	12.6
40.	"Loving Couples"	CBS	12.4
41.	"Apocalypse Now"	ABC	12.4
42.	"Survival Anglia"	CBS	12.0
43.	Gimme a Break	NBC	12.0
44.	Knight Rider	NBC	11.8
45.	Hunter	NBC	11.6
46.	"Anything for a Laugh"	ABC	11.6
47.	T. J. Hooker	ABC	11.5
48.	Double Trouble	NBC	11.5
49.	Magnum, P. I.	CBS	11.4
50.	Diff'rent Strokes	NBC	10.7
51.	Benson	ABC	10.7
52.	"Ray Mancini Story"	CBS	10.6
53.	Mike Hammer	CBS	10.5
54.	Webster	ABC	10.4
55.	Under One Roof	NBC	10.4
56.	Half-Nelson	NBC	10.4
57.	Double Dare	CBS	9.6
58.	Best Times	NBC	9.5
59.	"Dr. No"	ABC	9.5
60.	Punky Brewster	NBC	9.0
61.	Ripley's Believe It or Not	ABC	8.5
62.	Cover Up	CBS	8.3
63.	Eye to Eye	ABC	8.3
64.	Street Hawk	ABC	7.9
65.	Silver Spoons	NBC	7.8
66.	Lucie Arnaz Show	CBS	7.5
67.	Jeffersons	CBS	7.1

Source: A.C. Nielsen Company.

The following instructions will teach you how to make a box plot of the ratings of the 67 programs:

Step 1   Find the median rating.

There are 67 ratings, thus the median will be the 34th show. The 34th show, *St. Elsewhere*, has a rating of 13.9.

Step 2   Find the median of the upper half.

There are 33 ratings above the median. The median of these ratings is at the 17th show. This show is *Sara* with a rating of 16.3. This number 16.3 is the upper quartile.

Step 3   Find the median of the lower half.

There are 33 ratings below the median. The median of these ratings is at the 51st show, which is *Benson* with a rating of 10.7. This number 10.7 is the lower quartile.

Step 4   Find the extremes.

The lowest rating is 7.1 and the highest is 25.5.

Step 5   Mark dots for the median, quartiles, and extremes below a number line.

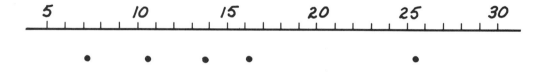

Step 6   Draw a box between the two quartiles. Mark the median with a line across the box. Draw two "whiskers" from the quartiles to the extremes.

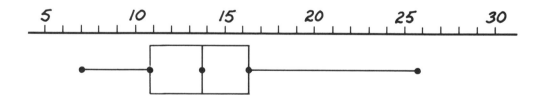

Discussion Questions

About what percent of the ratings are:

1. Below the median?

2. Below the lower quartile?

3. Above the lower quartile?

4. In the box?

5. In each whisker?

6. Is one whisker longer than the other? What does this mean?

7. Why isn't the median in the center of the box?

8. On May 8, 1985, CBS announced that it was cancelling *The Jeffersons, Cover Up, The Lucie Arnaz Show,* and *Double Dare*. The future of *Mike Hammer* was in doubt. Why do you think CBS is cancelling these shows? Are there any other programs CBS should consider cancelling?

9. Which shows do you think ABC cancelled?

The executives of the networks are interested in how the three compare in ratings. We learned that a back-to-back stem-and-leaf plot is good for such comparisons. Unfortunately, it has only two sides and there are three networks. Box plots are effective for comparing two or more sets of data. For example, let's plot the ratings for CBS, NBC, and ABC on separate box plots.

CBS has 22 shows listed. Their ratings are:

21.4	18.4	18.3	17.9	17.8	17.6	16.3	15.7
15.4	15.2	15.0	14.6	12.7	12.4	12.0	11.4
10.6	10.5	9.6	8.3	7.5	7.1		

The median is halfway between the 11th and 12th ratings, which are 15.0 and 14.6. Thus, the median is:

$$\frac{15.0 + 14.6}{2} = \frac{29.6}{2} = 14.8 \ .$$

The lower quartile is 10.6 and the upper quartile is 17.6. The extremes are 7.1 and 21.4.

The box plots for CBS, NBC, and ABC are shown below.

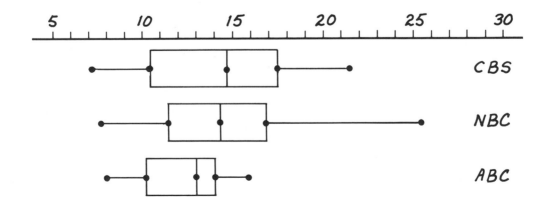

Discussion Questions

1. Use the box plot to estimate the median, quartiles, and extremes for NBC.

2. Use the box plot to estimate the median, quartiles, and extremes for ABC.

3. Study the box plots to decide which network has the largest interquartile range.

4. If you say that the winning network is the one with the highest-rated show, which network is the winner? Which is second? Which is third?

5. If you say that the winning network is the one with the largest upper quartile, which network is the winner? Which is second? Which is third?

6. If you say that the winning network is the one with the largest median, which network is the winner? Which is second? Which is third?

7. Use the box plot to estimate if there are any outliers for NBC. (Hint: The length of the box is one interquartile range!)

8. Are any shows outliers for CBS or ABC?

9. Why are box plots a better way to compare the relative positions of the three networks than line plots or stem-and-leaf plots?

10. Write a description of the relative standings of the three networks. Then (don't peek) read the following example.

The median ratings of the three networks are very close — each around 14. The lower quartiles and lower extremes are also very close — around 11 and 7, respectively. This means that if you look at just the shows in the bottom half for each network, the three networks do about the same in the ratings. However, when looking at the top half of the ratings, NBC and CBS do much better than ABC. The ratings for ABC are all packed tightly between 13.0 and 15.9. In contrast, about 25% of the ratings for both CBS and NBC are larger than 17. It is clear that ABC is the losing network, but whether NBC or CBS is the winner is not so clear.

Even if ABC had cancelled the bottom quarter of their shows and replaced them all by shows that received a higher rating than their current top show — for example between 17 and 22 — they would still be a bit behind NBC and CBS in terms of the top shows. (As an exercise, redraw the boxplot for ABC to reflect this hypothetical situation.)

Prices of Corn Poppers

The box plot below shows the dollar prices of twenty popcorn poppers as listed in *Consumer Reports Buying Guide*, 1981.

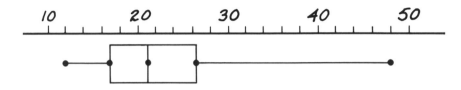

Source: *Consumer Reports Buying Guide*, 1981.

1. Approximately how much did the most expensive popcorn popper cost?

2. Approximately how much did the least expensive popcorn popper cost?

3. What was the median price for a popcorn popper?

4. What percentage of the poppers cost more than $26.50 (the upper quartile)?

5. What percentage of the poppers cost more than $17.00 (the lower quartile)?

6. If you had $21.00, how many of the twenty poppers could you afford?

7. If you had $26.50, how many of the twenty poppers could you afford?

8. Are any of the prices outliers? How can you tell?

9. Write a short description of the price of popcorn poppers.

Application 13

Roller Skating Clubs

The following table gives the number of roller skating clubs by state for 45 states.

State	Number	State	Number
Alabama	11	Nebraska	8
Arizona	6	Nevada	1
Arkansas	5	New Hampshire	1
California	102	New Jersey	24
Colorado	11	New Mexico	1
Connecticut	7	New York	18
Delaware	2	North Carolina	15
Florida	39	Ohio	47
Georgia	8	Oklahoma	5
Hawaii	1	Oregon	13
Illinois	35	Pennsylvania	41
Indiana	21	Rhode Island	5
Iowa	7	South Carolina	2
Kansas	7	Tennessee	10
Kentucky	6	Texas	40
Louisiana	10	Utah	2
Maine	1	Vermont	1
Maryland	15	Virginia	33
Massachusetts	13	Washington	22
Michigan	29	West Virginia	4
Minnesota	4	Wisconsin	8
Mississippi	3	Wyoming	2
Missouri	22		

Source: Roller Skating Rink Operators Association.

1. Why do you think the data include only 45 and not 50 states? What values might the 5 remaining states have? Which states are missing?

2. Make a box plot of the 45 values. (Hint: The numbers must be put in order before you find the median and the quartiles. A quick way to do this is to use a stem-and-leaf plot.)

3. Show that California is an outlier.

4. Look at the upper whisker. Why is it so long? If you were to omit California from the list, how would the box plot change?

5. There is an alternate way to construct the box plot when there is an outlier, such as California. Copy your box plot, but stop the upper whisker at Ohio's 47. Then, put an asterisk at California's 102. Thus, there is a gap in the plot, corresponding to the gap between the largest and second-largest values.

6. Which of these plots do you think gives a more accurate picture of these data? Why?

7. Write a description of the information given in the box plot you constructed for question 5.

Application 14

Sugar in Cereals

Percentage of Sugar in Cereals

Product	% Sugar	Product	% Sugar
Sugar Smacks (K)	56.0	Kellogg Raisin Bran (A)	29.0
Apple Jacks (K)	54.6	C. W. Post, Raisin, (A)	29.0
Froot Loops (K)	48.0	C. W. Post (A)	28.7
General Foods Raisin Bran (A)	48.0	Frosted Mini Wheats (K)	26.0
Sugar Corn Pops (K)	46.0	Country Crisp (K)	22.0
Super Sugar Crisp (K)	46.0	Life, cinnamon (K)	21.0
Crazy Cow, chocolate (K)	45.6	100% Bran (A)	21.0
Corny Snaps (K)	45.5	All Bran (A)	19.0
Frosted Rice Krinkles (K)	44.0	Fortified Oat Flakes (A)	18.5
Frankenberry (K)	43.7	Life (A)	16.0
Cookie Crisp, vanilla (K)	43.5	Team (A)	14.1
Cap'n Crunch, crunch berries (K)	43.3	40% Bran (A)	13.0
Cocoa Krispies (K)	43.0	Grape Nuts Flakes (A)	13.3
Cocoa Pebbles (K)	42.6	Buckwheat (A)	12.2
Fruity Pebbles (K)	42.5	Product 19 (A)	9.9
Lucky Charms (K)	42.2	Concentrate (A)	9.3
Cookie Crisp, chocolate (K)	41.0	Total (A)	8.3
Sugar Frosted Flakes of Corn (K)	41.0	Wheaties (A)	8.2
Quisp (K)	40.7	Rice Krispies (K)	7.8
Crazy Cow, strawberry (K)	40.1	Grape Nuts (A)	7.0
Cookie Crisp, oatmeal (K)	40.1	Special K (A)	5.4
Cap'n Crunch (K)	40.0	Corn Flakes (A)	5.3
Count Chocula (K)	39.5	Post Toasties (A)	5.0
Alpha Bits (K)	38.0	Kix (K)	4.8
Honey Comb (K)	37.2	Rice Chex (A)	4.4
Frosted Rice (K)	37.0	Corn Chex (A)	4.0
Trix (K)	35.9	Wheat Chex (A)	3.5
Cocoa Puffs (K)	33.3	Cheerios (K)	3.0
Cap'n Crunch, peanut butter (K)	32.2	Shredded Wheat (A)	0.6
Golden Grahams (A)	30.0	Puffed Wheat (A)	0.5
Cracklin' Bran (A)	29.0	Puffed Rice (A)	0.1

Source: United States Department of Agriculture, 1979.

1. What do you think the table means when it says that "the percentage of sugar" in Sugar Smacks is 56.0?

We divided the list into "kid" and "adult" cereals as indicated by a (K) or an (A) following each name. (You may disagree and change some of these.)

The following box plots show the amount of sugar in "kid" and "adult" cereals.

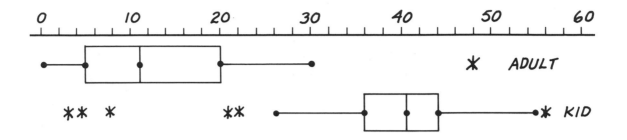

2. For the "kid" cereals, estimate:

    a. the lower extreme

    b. the upper extreme

    c. the median

    d. the lower quartile

    e. the upper quartile

3. For the "adult" cereals, estimate

    a. the lower extreme

    b. the upper extreme

    c. the median

    d. the lower quartile

    e. the upper quartile

4. Write a paragraph comparing the percentage of sugar in "kid" and "adult" cereals.

Application 15

Automobile Safety

The Highway Loss Data Institute rated 181 models of 1982-84 cars based on the number of insurance claims filed for personal injury coverage. The cars are rated in relative terms; 100 represents the average for all cars. Lower numbers mean a better safety record. A rating of 122, for example, means 22% worse than average.

Station Wagons and Passenger Vans

Small Cars	Injury Rating	Midsize Cars	Injury Rating	Large Cars	Injury Rating
Volkswagen Vanagon	73	Volvo 240	56	Olds. Custom Cruiser	54
Mercury Lynx	83	American Eagle 30	69	Buick Electra	59
Toyota Tercel 4WD	91	Ford LTD	76	Dodge Caravan	63
Ford Escort	95	Oldsmobile Firenza	80	Plymouth Voyager	67
Subaru DL/GL 4WD	98	Chevrolet Celebrity	83	Chevrolet Caprice	69
Subaru DL/GL	100	Dodge Aries	91	Mercury Grand Marquis	69
Nissan Sentra	108	Plymouth Reliant	93	Ford Crown Victoria	70
		Pontiac 2000	94		
		Chevrolet Cavalier	94		
		Chrysler LeBaron	95		
		Nissan Maxima	100		

Source: Highway Loss Data Institute.

Sports and Specialty Models

Small Cars	Injury Rating	Midsize Cars	Injury Rating	Large Cars	Injury Rating
Mercedes 380SL Coupe	57	Lincoln Continental	72	Mercedes 300SD/380SE	60
Chevrolet Corvette	63	BMW 528e/533i	74	Jaguar X16	63
Porsche 944 Coupe	71	Audi 5000 4D	79	Mercedes-Benz 300D	64
Nissan 300ZX	100	BMW 318i/325e	81	Oldsmobile Toronado	65
VW Rabbit Convertible	102	Chrys. LeBaron Conv.	87	Cadillac De Ville 4D	67
Mazda RX-7	104	Ford Mustang Convertible	98	Cadillac Eldorado	71
Pontiac Fiero	119	Toyota Celica Supra	102	Lincoln Town Car	72
Ford EXP	124	Pontiac Firebird	107	Buick Riviera	73
		Mercury Capri	114	Cadillac Brougham 4D	75
		Chevrolet Camaro	116	Cadillac Seville	76
		Ford Mustang	127	Cadillac De Ville 2D	81

Source: Highway Loss Data Institute.

Four-Door Models

Small Cars	Injury Ratings	Midsize Cars	Injury Ratings	Large Cars	Injury Ratings
Saab 900	71	Chrysler E Class	75	Oldsmobile Delta 88	59
Honda Accord	89	Oldsmobile Cutlass	76	Buick LeSabre	62
Volkswagen Rabbit	92	Buick Regal	79	Oldsmobile Ninety Eight	62
Volkswagen Jetta	97	Pontiac Bonneville	80	Mercury Grand Marquis	65
Mazda 626	100	Mercury Topaz	81	Buick Electra	66
Nissan Stanza	107	Pontiac 6000	85	Chevrolet Caprice	68
Dodge Omni	114	Mercury Marquis	86	Ford LTD Crown Victoria	68
Renault Alliance	114	Dodge 600	86	Chrys. 5th Ave.	69
Ford Escort	117	Oldsmobile Ciera	86	Dodge Diplomat	72
Plymouth Horizon	118	Chrysler New Yorker	87	Chevrolet Impala	79
Mercury Lynx	120	Buick Century	87	Plymouth Grand Fury	101
Toyota Corolla	122	Chrysler LeBaron	88		
Subaru DL/GL Sedan	125	Volvo 240	89		
Toyota Tercel	127	Ford LTD	89		
Mazda GLC	130	Peugeot 505	91		
Pontiac 1000	139	Toyota Camry	91		
Isuzu T-Car/I-Mark	140	Toyota Cressida	92		
Chevrolet Chevette	143	Buick Skylark	92		
Dodge Colt	144	Cadillac Cimarron	93		
Nissan Sentra	145	Chevrolet Celebrity	94		
Mitsubishi Tredia	155	Chevrolet Citation	94		
Plymouth Colt	156	Audi 4000	96		
		Oldsmobile Omega	98		
		Ford Tempo	100		
		Pontiac Phoenix	101		
		Pontiac 2000	109		
		Dodge Aries	111		
		Plymouth Reliant	112		
		Chevrolet Cavalier	112		
		Oldsmobile Firenza	113		
		Buick Skyhawk	113		
		Nissan Maxima	121		

Source: Highway Loss Data Institute.

Two-Door Models

Small Cars	Injury Ratings	Midsize Cars	Injury Ratings	Large Cars	Injury Ratings
Saab 900	70	Oldsmobile Cutlass	88	Ford Crown Victoria	65
Honda Accord	102	Buick Regal	90	Buick LeSabre	70
Nissan Stanza	105	Oldsmobile Ciera	91	Oldsmobile Delta 88	70
Volkswagen Rabbit	106	Pontiac Grand Prix	92	Oldsmobile Ninety Eight	71
Mazda 626	106	Oldsmobile Omega	92	Mercury Grand Marquis	76
Volkswagen Scirocco	108	Pontiac 6000	94	Chevrolet Caprice	77
Mazda GLC	110	Buick Skylark	94	Buick Electra	81
Honda Prelude	114	Chevrolet Monte Carlo	98		
Honda Civic	115	Chrysler LeBaron	99		
Subaru Hardtop	117	Ford Thunderbird	100		
Renault Fuego	118	Buick Century	100		
Toyota Celica	120	Volvo 240	104		
Dodge Daytona	122	Dodge 400/600	105		
Subaru Hatchback	125	Chevrolet Celebrity	107		
Plymouth Horizon	128	Dodge Aries	109		
Chrysler Laser	128	Mercury Cougar	109		
Toyota Tercel	129	Chevrolet Citation	111		
Ford Escort	130	Pontiac Phoenix	112		
Renault Encore	130	Pontiac 2000	118		
Dodge Charger	132	Ford Tempo	118		
Mercury Lynx	137	Plymouth Reliant	119		
Nissan Sentra	137	Buick Skylark	123		
Renault Alliance	138	Oldsmobile Firenza	123		
Toyota Starlet	148	Chevrolet Cavalier	126		
Plymouth Colt	148				
Dodge Colt	149				
Mitsubishi Cordia	151				
Chevrolet Chevette	154				
Pontiac 1000	155				
Nissan Pulsar	158				

Source: Highway Loss Data Institute.

1. Which of the four groups of cars is the safest?

2. Which is the most dangerous group?

67

3. The box plot for all of the small cars and for midsize cars is shown below. (All four types of models were combined.) Make the box plot for large cars. Show any outliers as in Application 13, question 5.

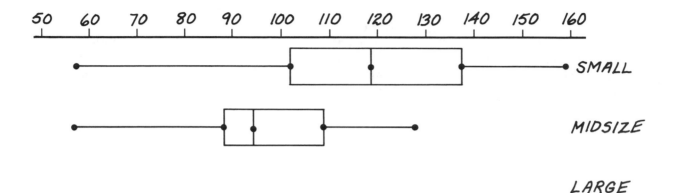

4. Which would you say are closer in safety, small and midsize cars, or midsize and large cars? Why?

5. Write a paragraph giving an overall summary of the plots.

6. (Optional) Make box plots for American small cars and for Japanese small cars, or two other categories that interest you, and write a summary of the plots.

7. (For class discussion) Do you think that these injury ratings reflect just the inherent safety of these cars? Might they also relate to other factors such as different characteristics of the drivers, different mileages, or different types of driving that the cars receive? What other ways can you think of for comparing the safety of different automobiles?

Application 16

High School Eligibility

Data from the *Los Angeles Times* appear in the following table.

High School	% Ineligible in Selected Activities					
	Band	Drama	Yearbook	Baseball	Boys Track	Girls Track
Banning	27	19	0	9	38	24
Bell	37	19	—	0	22	13
Belmont	—	3	7	19	14	7
Birmingham	52	31	—	—	24	—
Canoga Park	30	19	20	17	25	33
Carson	—	0	—	13	21	—
Chatsworth	25	19	33	9	20	31
Cleveland	11	—	7	16	15	—
Crenshaw	68	36	—	20	19	17
Dorsey	8	28	—	15	31	31
Eagle Rock	0	—	0	—	—	—
El Camino Real	7	15	13	3	16	15
Fairfax	35	23	—	21	51	30
Francis Poly	4	28	—	0	22	31
Franklin	48	33	21	17	29	44
Fremont	—	43	—	32	32	38
Gardena	34	—	17	19	20	20
Garfield	21	—	—	7	16	23
Granada Hills	14	29	—	15	21	28
Grant	—	3	—	17	26	—
Hamilton	36	27	0	24	12	0
Hollywood	3	3	8	—	—	—
Huntington Park	40	33	44	15	22	—
Jefferson	61	58	—	8	62	—

High School	% Ineligible in Selected Activities					
	Band	Drama	Yearbook	Baseball	Boys Track	Girls Track
Jordan	49	70	50	38	32	—
Kennedy	20	14	18	0	18	20
Lincoln	32	28	71	6	17	13
Locke	30	—	67	45	30	57
Los Angeles	27	100	39	43	37	17
Manual Arts	45	35	38	21	18	25
Marshall	14	19	—	16	31	15
Monroe	23	30	6	3	21	24
Narbonne	21	35	0	—	—	—
North Hollywood	18	50	—	—	—	—
Palisades	4	14	—	14	30	30
Reseda	24	53	0	—	—	—
Roosevelt	—	39	—	12	12	35
San Fernando	19	64	24	24	44	33
San Pedro	11	10	—	8	18	0
South Gate	38	8	5	19	15	28
Sylmar	10	32	—	0	21	13
Taft	—	11	0	10	27	27
University	20	30	43	16	14	9
Van Nuys	22	21	0	17	30	7
Venice	11	21	—	5	16	13
Verdugo Hills	8	35	10	14	39	39
Washington	29	31	25	16	18	14
Westchester	19	11	0	17	3	0
Wilson	—	—	—	—	—	—

Source: *Los Angeles Times*, May 17, 1983.

Following a policy established by the Los Angeles Board of Education, students must maintain a C average and have no failing grades in order to participate in extracurricular activities. The table shows how the policy is affecting activities at high schools. Numbers represent the percentage of students in the activity who were declared ineligible. For example, 25% of band members at Chatsworth and 38% of the athletes in girls' track at Fremont were declared ineligible and could no longer participate.

1. The newspaper does not say why the table contains blanks. How do you know that a blank does not mean that no students were ineligible? What do you think a blank means? For the rest of this activity , ignore the blanks.

2. The class should be divided into six groups. One group should construct a box plot of the percentage of students declared ineligible in band; one group should construct the plot for drama; another for yearbook, and so on. Use an asterisk for any outliers, as in Application 13, question 5.

3. Make a number line on the blackboard or overhead projector. A representative from each group should draw its box plot under this number line.

4. Do band members or baseball players tend to have higher rates of ineligibility?

5. Why is there no lower whisker on the yearbook box plot?

6. Write a paragraph or two summarizing what you see in the six box plots.

The Use of Box Plots

It is becoming more and more common to use a box plot to tell people their results on a test. For example, students sometimes take tests to see how interested they are in various occupations. The results from one such test are reproduced below.

BASIC INTEREST SCALES

Let's examine the "Nature" result more carefully. There are two box plots for "Nature." The top one is for girls and the bottom one is for boys. The top box plot shows that the median interest score in nature for girls is about 51. (The scale is above "Mechanical Activities.") The score of the girl who took the test is marked on each scale by a ★. Thus, her interest in nature is very low compared to other girls who have taken the test previously.

Discussion Questions

1. For which subject(s) is this girl's interest score in the top 25% of all girls?

2. For which subjects is this girl's interest lowest?

3. Which subjects are girls much more interested in than are boys?

4. Which subjects are boys much more interested in than are girls?

5. Write a letter to this girl recommending possible career choices.

Box Plots — Summary

You may have found it difficult to see the advantages of using box plots. Some students are disturbed by the fact that most of the data disappears and only five summary numbers (the median, quartiles, and extremes) remain. It is true that we can no longer spot clusters and gaps, nor can we identify the shape of the distribution as clearly as with line plots or stem-and-leaf plots. However, we are able to focus on the relative positions of different sets of data and thereby compare them more easily.

Box plots are especially useful when the set of data contains hundreds or even thousands of numbers. A line plot or stem-and-leaf plot would be unwieldy with thousands of numbers on it!

To compare two (or more) sets of data using box plots, first look at the boxes to get an idea whether or not they are located in about the same place. Also, study their lengths, to determine whether or not the variabilities in the data sets are about the same. Then, you can focus on details. Check whether or not one data set has median, upper and lower quartiles, and extremes that are all larger than the corresponding values in the second data set. If it does, then the data in the first set tend to be larger than those in the second no matter which criterion we use for comparing them. If it does not, then there is more uncertainty about which data set is larger. In either case, the plot has helped us learn some details about the similarities and differences between the two data sets. Also, check to see if the pattern of outliers is the same in both data sets.

Notice that even if two (or more) sets of data have unequal numbers of values, this does not cause problems for making comparisons with box plots. This was not true for stem-and-leaf plots.

Suggestions for Student Projects

1. Collect some data on a topic that interests you, construct box plots, and interpret them. Topics that other students have used include:

   • number of hours students work per week

   • number of hours of TV watched per week by different types of students

   • allowances of girls and of boys in your class

   • scores of all the students in a school that take a certain test, separated so you can compare the different classes

2. One variation of box plots involves changing the width in proportion to the number of data values represented. For example, if a box representing 100 values is 1 cm wide, then a box representing 50 values would be 0.5 cm wide and a box representing 200 values would be 2 cm wide. Make box plots under the same number line for the small two-door models, midsize two-door models and large two-door models from Application 15. Make the width of the box proportional to the number of cars represented. Discuss the merit of this variation.

V. REVIEW OF ONE-VARIABLE TECHNIQUES

Which Method to Use?

This section is different from the previous four. Each of the previous four introduced some statistical method that can help to interpret data. Then, the method was used on several examples. Often more than one of these methods *could* be used to display and to help interpret a particular set of data. This section helps you to choose an appropriate method by giving some comparisons among them.

Before using any statistical method it is a good idea to ask yourself a few basic questions about the data. How were the numbers obtained? Are the values plausible? What would you like to learn from the data? Are there any specific questions that you know need answers? The purpose of statistical methods is to help us learn something useful or interesting from the data, so it is a good idea to keep questions such as these in mind throughout the analysis.

Suppose we have the starting weekly wage for 23 different jobs. We could display the values using a line plot (Section I), a stem-and-leaf plot (Section II), or a box plot (Section IV). We could calculate statistics such as the median, mean, range, and interquartile range (Section III). Which of these methods should we use, or, at least, which should we use first? There is no single, correct answer. However, there are some guidelines that can help you to make an appropriate choice of methods.

A reasonable general strategy is to use the simpler methods first. Then, if the interpretations of the data are very clear, there is no need to go on to more complicated displays and methods.

One Group and One Variable

Consider the above example of the starting wage for several jobs. In this example there is one *variable*, the wage. We can treat the various jobs as forming one *group* of jobs. Thus, we have measurements for *one group on one variable*. This is the simplest type of problem for which statistical methods and displays are needed. Most of the examples in Sections I, II, and III are this type of problem.

The line plot, the stem-and-leaf plot, and the box plot are three different displays that can be used for the one-group/one-variable situation. The following paragraphs describe their relative advantages and disadvantages.

Line Plot. The line plot is easy to construct and interpret. It gives a clear graphical picture, and a few values can be labeled easily. Constructing a line plot is also a useful first step for calculating the median, extremes, and quartiles. These statements are all true providing the number of values is not too large — fewer than about 25. As the number of values becomes larger, the line plot can become unwieldy and more difficult to interpret. When a specific value is repeated several times or when there are many nearby values, the line plot can also become jumbled. Another disadvantage is that it is hard to read the exact numerical values from the line plot. In conclusion, the line plot is a useful first display for the one-group/one-variable situation, providing there are about 25 or fewer values in the data.

Stem-and-Leaf Plot. The stem-and-leaf plot shares many advantages of the line plot. It is easy to construct and interpret, values can be labeled, and it is a useful first step for calculating the median, extremes, and quartiles. In addition, exact numerical values can be read from the stem-and-leaf plot and repeated values and nearby values in the data cause no special problems. Stem-and-leaf plots do not get as unwieldy as line plots when the number of data values becomes large. On the other hand, a disadvantage is that to construct the stem-and-leaf plot you may have to decide whether or not to truncate or round. Further disadvantages are the need to decide which values to use for the stems, and how to spread out the plot. Thus, it may take more thought to construct the stem-and-leaf plot than the line plot. The stem-and-leaf plot can display more values than the line plot without becoming too confusing in appearance. However, it also has a limit to the number of values that is *reasonable* to display. With more than about 100 values, you will most likely spread out the stem-and-leaf plot. Then it can be useful for up to about 250 values. Above 250 it will be too large and jumbled to interpret easily. In conclusion, for the one-group/one-variable situation with about 25 or fewer values, either the stem-and-leaf plot or the line plot is a reasonable first display. The choice is partly a matter of personal preference. With about 25 to 250 data values, the stem-and-leaf plot is the most useful first display.

Box Plot. The box plot is more complicated to construct, since you must calculate the median, extremes, and quartiles first. Generally, the simplest way to do this is to construct the stem-and-leaf plot first and then count in from the ends to get the quartiles and median. Unlike the stem-and-leaf plot, once the box plot is constructed, specific data values cannot be read from it (except for outliers and the median, quartiles, and extremes). The main advantage of the box plot is that it is not cluttered by showing all the data values. It highlights only a few *important* features of the data. Thus, the box plot makes it easier to focus attention on the median, extremes, and quartiles and comparisons among them. Another advantage of the box plot is that it does not become more complicated with more data values. It is useful with any number of values. A disadvantage of the box plot occurs when there are only a few data values — less than about 15. Then, the plotted values might change greatly if only one or a few of the observations were changed.

The box plot is a *summary display* since it shows only certain statistics, not all the data. In conclusion, the box plot is not as useful as the line or stem-and-leaf plots for showing details, but it enables us to focus more easily on the median, extremes, and quartiles. Since the line and stem-and-leaf plots are useful for computing the statistics needed to construct the box plot, it is generally reasonable to make one of these two plots first even if you will eventually construct and use the box plot.

Several Groups and One Variable

Think again about the starting weekly wage example mentioned at the beginning of this section. Instead of considering the 23 jobs as *one group* of jobs, we could divide them into those jobs that require a high school diploma and those that require a college diploma. The jobs are divided into *two groups*. We want to compare the various salaries in these two groups. This is an example of the *two-group/one-variable* problem. Many of the examples in Sections II and IV are this type. The following paragraphs describe the relative advantages and disadvantages of the line, stem-and-leaf, and box plots for this situation.

Line plots can be placed next to each other to compare two groups, although we did not give any examples of this type. However, this becomes confusing if the two groups overlap a lot or if there are more than a total of about 25 data values.

Back-to-back stem-and-leaf plots are more useful for comparing two groups. They are easy to construct. Comparisons can be made by judging the number of leaves for various stems. However, if the number of data values in the two groups is not roughly equal, the comparisons get more difficult. The details shown in the stem-and-leaf plots can become an obstacle. Furthermore, as the number of values becomes large these plots become unwieldy. In summary, for comparing two groups of about equal size with around 100 or fewer data values in each group, back-to-back stem-and-leaf plots are easy to construct and generally adequate.

Box plots below the same number line can also be used to compare two groups. This gives the easiest and most direct comparisons of the two minimums, the two lower quartiles, the two medians, the two upper quartiles, and the two maximums. Of course, this does not show any other details, but these quantities are usually sufficient for comparing two groups. Moreover, there are no special problems caused by having a large number of data values, or by having a different number of values in the two groups.

Often, we need to compare more than two groups. For example, the jobs could be broken down into those not requiring a high school diploma, those requiring a high school diploma, those requiring a college degree, and those requiring a graduate degree. This gives four groups. It is an example of a *many-group/one-variable* problem.

There is no way to construct a stem-and-leaf plot for this situation. Several line plots placed next to each other can be useful, if there are not many data values. Box plots are the best choice. The reasons are the same as those given for comparing two groups.

A more concise way to compare two groups than any of these is simply to calculate a single number, such as the mean or median, for each group. But this number hides all the other information in the data. It also loses the advantage of graphical displays. Thus, for purposes of exploring and interpreting data, any of the graphical displays will be more valuable than calculating just means or medians. If it is necessary to give a single number to summarize the data, and if there is a possibility of even a few outliers, then the median is usually more valuable than the mean.

As a general conclusion, line plots, stem-and-leaf plots, and box plots each have a useful role for exploring various kinds of data sets. Often, it is worthwhile to make more than one plot. There are no hard and fast rules about which plot should be used, but the previous comparisons can help you make good choices.

The following applications will help you compare the different methods.

Application 17

Letter Frequencies

The number of occurrences of each letter was counted in a very large amount of written material. The percentage that each letter occurred is given in the table below.

A	8.2	J	0.1	S	6.0
B	1.4	K	0.4	T	10.5
C	2.8	L	3.4	U	2.5
D	3.8	M	2.5	V	0.9
E	13.0	N	7.0	W	1.5
F	3.0	O	8.0	X	0.2
G	2.0	P	2.0	Y	2.0
H	5.3	Q	0.1	Z	0.07
I	6.5	R	6.8		

Source: National Council of Teachers of Mathematics.

1. What is the most-used letter?

2. What is the least-used letter?

3. How many *t*'s would you expect to find in a paragraph of 100 letters? In a paragraph of 500 letters?

4. As a group, vowels account for what percentage of letters used?

5. Make a line plot of the percentages.

6. Make a stem-and-leaf plot of the percentages.

7. Find the median percentage, the quartiles, and any outliers.

8. Make a box plot of the percentages.

9. Which two letters have the most unusual percentages? From which plot is it easiest to find this information?

10. Are most of the letters used rarely or used more frequently? From which plot is it easiest to find this information?

11. Make a back-to-back stem-and-leaf plot of vowels and consonants.

12. Why isn't it appropriate to make one box plot for vowels and another for consonants?

13. What conclusions can you make by looking at the stem-and-leaf plot you constructed for question 11?

Salaries

The table below lists the median weekly salaries of workers employed full time. For example, the median salary for carpenters is $325 because half of the carpenters earn less than $325 and half earn more than $325.

Occupation	Median Weekly Earnings	Occupation	Median Weekly Earnings
Accountant	379	Machinist	356
Airplane Pilot	530	Mathematician	508
Architect	428	Newspaper Reporter	351
Auto Mechanic	285	Painter	271
Bank Teller	189	Pharmacist	463
Barber	327	Physician, Osteopath	501
Bookkeeper	227	Plumber	404
Carpenter	325	Police Officer	363
Cashier	168	Postal Clerk	400
Chemist	467	Printing Press Operator	320
Civil Engineer	505	Psychologist	394
College Teacher	444	Receptionist	200
Computer Programmer	422	Registered Nurse	332
Cooks and Chefs	171	Retail Sales Worker	178
Cosmetologist	179	School Counselor	396
Dental Assistant	183	Secondary Teacher	351
Dentist	352	Secretary	229
Drafter	343	Shoe Repairer	200
Electrician	419	Telephone Operator	240
Fire Fighter	362	Truck Driver (local)	314
Flight Attendant	365	Truck Driver (long distance)	517
Food Counter Worker	141	Typist	213
K-6 Teacher	322	Veterinarian	656
Lawyer	546	Waiter/Waitress	150
Librarian	320	Welder	334

Source: United States Bureau of Labor Statistics.

1. Which kind of worker earns the most?

2. Which kind of worker earns the least?

3. Which occupation listed would you most like to have someday?

4. Suppose you want to see how the salary of the occupation you chose compares to the other salaries. Which do you think is best for this use: a line plot, stem-and-leaf plot, or box plot?

5. Construct the plot you selected.

6. In one or two sentences, describe how the salary of the occupation you chose compares to the other salaries.

Application 19

Money Spent Per Student

The values in the table below are the amount of money spent on education per student in 1983-84 for each of the 50 states and Washington, D.C.

State	Expense	State	Expense
Alabama	$2,082	Montana	$3,691
Alaska	$6,378	Nebraska	$2,913
Arizona	$2,685	Nevada	$2,882
Arkansas	$2,214	New Hampshire	$2,765
California	$2,981	New Jersey	$4,677
Colorado	$3,188	New Mexico	$2,866
Connecticut	$4,055	New York	$4,821
Delaware	$3,848	North Carolina	$2,455
D.C.	$4,574	North Dakota	$2,952
Florida	$3,169	Ohio	$2,996
Georgia	$2,317	Oklahoma	$3,146
Hawaii	$3,395	Oregon	$3,771
Idaho	$2,174	Pennsylvania	$3,707
Illinois	$3,384	Rhode Island	$3,811
Indiana	$2,583	South Carolina	$2,271
Iowa	$3,251	South Dakota	$2,639
Kansas	$3,392	Tennessee	$2,141
Kentucky	$2,646	Texas	$2,960
Louisiana	$2,707	Utah	$2,047
Maine	$2,839	Vermont	$3,491
Maryland	$3,771	Virginia	$2,853
Massachusetts	$3,692	Washington	$3,129
Michigan	$3,315	West Virginia	$2,488
Minnesota	$3,322	Wisconsin	$3,677
Mississippi	$2,090	Wyoming	$4,488
Missouri	$2,814		

Source: National Education Association.

1. Using the value for your state, and an estimate of the number of students in your school, give a rough estimate of the total cost of running your school in 1983-84.

2. Suppose you want to know how your state compares to the others. Construct a plot to help you make this comparison, and label your state.

Then, write a paragraph describing the overall distribution of expenses, and the relative position of your state.

3. Pick 3 to 5 nearby states that are similar to yours. Label them on the plot. Write another sentence or two describing how the expenses in your state compare to those of your neighbors.

4. Using the map of the United States on page 15, classify each state as being in the Northeast, Central, South, or West. Then, construct a plot to show how the expenses per student compare in the four regions of the country. Write a paragraph summarizing the comparisons.

VI. SCATTER PLOTS

The table below gives the box score for the first game of the 1985 National Basketball Association Championship series.

Los Angeles Lakers 114, Boston Celtics 148							
LOS ANGELES							
	Min	FG-A	FT-A	R	A	P	T
Worthy	37	8-19	4-6	8	5	1	20
Rambis	22	4-6	0-0	9	0	2	8
Jabbar	22	6-11	0-0	3	1	3	12
Magic Johnson	34	8-14	3-4	1	12	2	19
Scott	30	5-14	0-0	2	0	2	10
Cooper	24	1-5	2-2	2	2	3	4
McAdoo	21	6-13	0-0	3	0	5	12
McGee	15	4-7	4-5	2	2	1	14
Spriggs	15	4-7	0-2	3	4	1	8
Kupchak	16	3-3	1-2	2	1	3	7
Lester	4	0-1	0-0	0	1	0	0
Totals	240	49-100	14-21	35	28	23	114
Shooting field goals, 49.0%, free throws, 66.7%							
BOSTON							
	Min	FG-A	FT-A	R	A	P	T
Bird	31	8-14	2-2	6	9	1	19
McHale	32	10-16	6-9	9	0	1	26
Parish	28	6-11	6-7	8	1	1	18
Dennis Johnson	33	6-14	1-1	3	10	1	13
Ainge	29	9-15	0-0	5	6	1	19
Buckner	16	3-5	0-0	4	6	4	6
Williams	14	3-5	0-0	0	5	2	6
Wedman	23	11-11	0-2	5	2	4	26
Maxwell	16	1-1	1-2	3	1	0	3
Kite	10	3-5	1-2	3	0	1	7
Carr	4	1-3	0-0	1	0	1	3
Clark	4	1-2	0-0	1	3	0	2
Totals	240	62-102	17-25	48	43	17	148
Shooting field goals, 60.8%, free throws, 68.0%							

	Key for table
Min	Minutes played
FG-A	Field goals made - field goals attempted
FT-A	Free throws made - free throws attempted
R	Rebounds
A	Assists
P	Personal fouls
T	Total points scored

Source: *Los Angeles Times*, May 28, 1985.

Discussion Questions

1. How many rebounds did Kevin McHale make?

2. Which player played the most minutes?

3. Which player had the most assists?

4. How many field goals did James Worthy make? How many did he attempt? What percentage did he make?

5. Five players are on the court at one time for each team. Determine how many minutes are in a game.

6. Which team made a larger percentage of free throws?

7. How is the T (total points scored) column computed? Verify that this number is correct for Magic Johnson and for Kevin McHale. (Caution: Some of the field goals for other players were three point shots.)

Do you think that the players who *attempt* the most field goals are generally the players that *make* the most field goals? Of course! We can see this from the box score. To further investigate this question, we will make a *scatter plot* showing field goals made (FG) and field goals attempted (FG-A). First, set up a plot with field goals attempted on the horizontal axis and field goals made on the vertical axis.

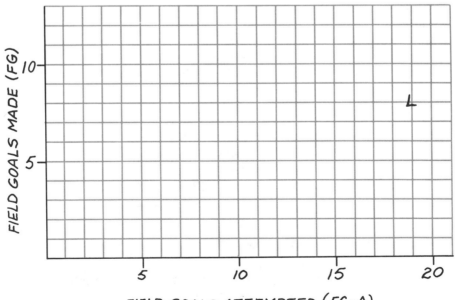

Worthy, the first player, attempted 19 field goals and made 8 of them. The L on the preceding plot represents Worthy. The L is above 19 and across from 8. We used an L to show that he is a Los Angeles player.

The completed scatter plot follows. Each B stands for a Boston player and each L for a Los Angeles player.

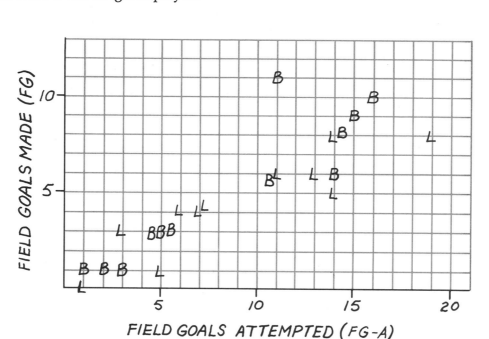

As we suspected, this plot shows that players who attempt more field goals generally make more field goals, and players who attempt few field goals make few field goals. Thus, there is a *positive* association between field goals attempted and field goals made.

However, we can see much more from this plot. First, a player who makes every basket will be represented by a point on the line through the points (0, 0), (1, 1), (2, 2), (3, 3), and so forth. Second, the players who are relatively far below this line were not shooting as well as the other players. Finally, we can observe the relative positions of the two teams in this plot.

Discussion Questions

1. Using the scatter plot, find the points that represent the three perfect shooters.

2. Why are all the points below a diagonal line running from lower left to upper right?

3. Is there a different pattern for Los Angeles and Boston players?

4. Which three Laker players were not shooting very well that game?

5. Suppose a player attempts 9 field goals. About how many would you expect him to make?

6. Write a brief description of the information conveyed by this scatter plot. Then read the following sample discussion. Did you notice any information not listed in this sample discussion?

In this plot, we were not surprised to see a positive association between the number of field goals attempted and the number of field goals made. There were three players, two from Boston and one from Los Angeles, who made all the field goals they attempted. One of these Boston players was truly outstanding as he made eleven out of eleven attempts. The Laker players who attempted a great number of field goals generally did not make as many of them as did the Celtics who attempted a great number of field goals. This could have been the deciding factor in the game.

The points seem to cluster into two groups. The cluster on the upper right generally contains players who played over 20 minutes and the one on the lower left contains players who played less than 20 minutes.

An assist is a pass that leads directly to a basket. A player is credited with a rebound when he recovers the ball following a missed shot. Do you think that players who get a lot of rebounds also make a lot of assists? It is difficult to answer this question just by looking at the box score.

To answer this question, we will make a scatter plot showing rebounds (R) and assists (A). This plot includes all players who made at least four rebounds or four assists.

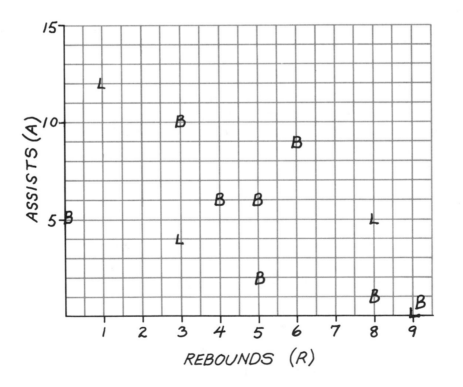

This plot shows that players who get *more* rebounds generally have *fewer* assists, and players who get *fewer* rebounds have *more* assists. Thus, there is a *negative* association between rebounds and assists.

Discussion Questions

1. Do the players who get the most rebounds also make the most assists?

2. Suppose a player had 7 rebounds. About how many assists would you expect this player to have?

3. Is there a different pattern for Boston players than for Los Angeles players?

4. Why do you suppose players who get a lot of rebounds do not make a lot of assists?

5. If you were the coach and you wanted a player to make more assists, would you instruct him to make fewer rebounds?

6. Why didn't we include players who would have been in the lower left-hand corner of this plot?

The following scatter plot shows total points and personal fouls for all players.

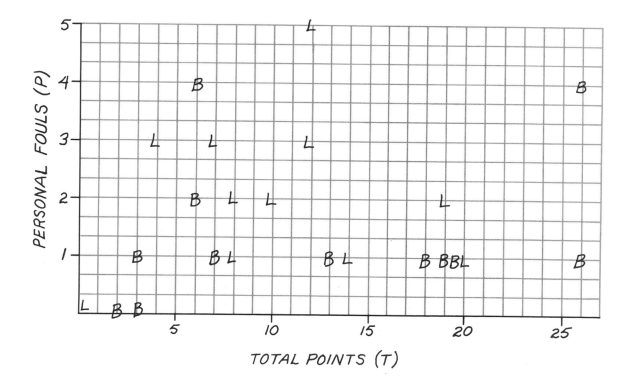

This plot shows *no association* between total points scored and the number of personal fouls committed.

In summary, the following scatter plots show *positive association*.

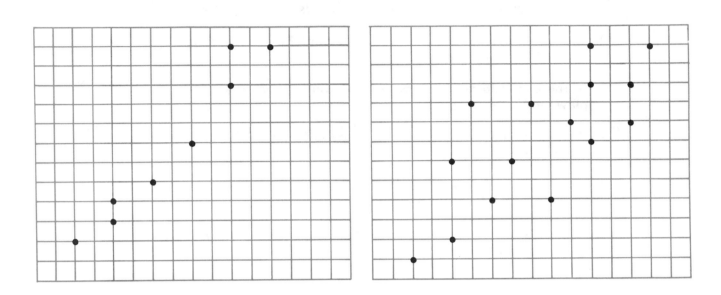

The following scatter plots show *negative association*.

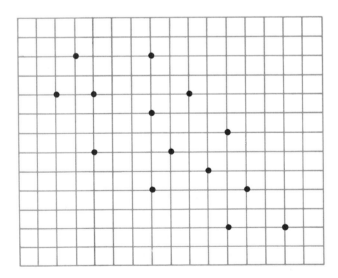
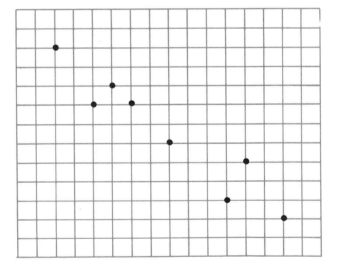

The following scatter plots show *no association*.

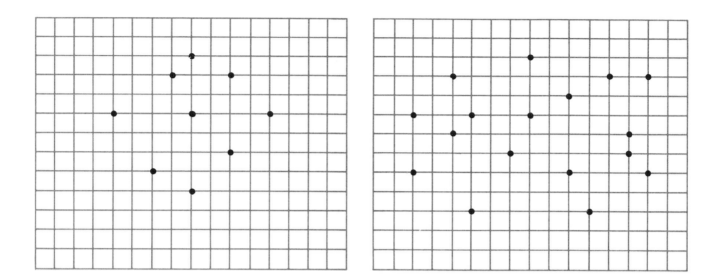

Sometimes one or two points can make it appear that there is a positive or negative association when there is really no association. If you can cover up one or two points and make it look as if there is no association, there probably really is none.

When describing the information displayed on a scatter plot, you can discuss

1. whether there is positive, negative, or no association;

2. whether there are any clusters of points and whether the points in the clusters have anything in common; and

3. whether any points do not follow the general pattern.

It's not always safe to conclude that one variable *causes* another to happen (or not happen) just because there is an association.

Box Office Hits

The table below shows production costs, promotion costs, and gross ticket sales for twelve of the most popular "dumb" movies. The box office grosses were obtained from studios and are estimates.

Dumbing for Dollars

	Year	Production Costs	Promotion Costs	Worldwide Ticket Sales
"Animal House"	1978	$2.9 million	$3 million	$150 million
"Meatballs"	1979	$1.4 million	$2 million	$70 million
"Caddyshack"	1980	$4.8 million	$4 million	$60 million
"Stripes"	1981	$10.5 million	$4.5 million	$85 million
"Spring Break"	1982	$4.5 million	$5 million	$24 million
"Porky's"	1982	$4.8 million	$9 million	$160 million
"Fast Times At Ridgemont High"	1982	$5 million	$4.9 million	$50 million
"Porky's II — The Next Day"	1983	$7 million	$7.5 million	$55 million
"Hot Dog — The Movie"	1984	$2 million	$4 million	$22 million
"Bachelor Party"	1984	$7 million	$7.5 million	$38 million
"Revenge of the Nerds"	1984	$7 million	$7.5 million	$42 million
"Police Academy"	1984	$4.5 million	$4 million	$150 million

Source: Peter H. Brown, "Dumbing for Dollars," *Los Angeles Times,* January 20, 1985.

The scatter plot for total costs (production costs + promotion costs) and worldwide ticket sales follows.

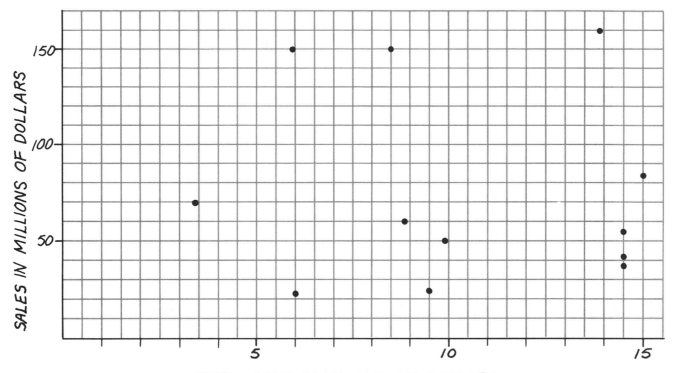

TOTAL COST IN MILLIONS OF DOLLARS

1. Is there positive association, negative association, or no association between total costs and worldwide ticket sales?

2. Which movie(s) would you say did the best when costs are compared to ticket sales?

3. Which movie(s) would you say did the worst when costs are compared to ticket sales?

4. Make a scatter plot of promotion costs against production costs. Put production costs on the horizontal axis and promotion costs on the vertical axis.

5. Is there a positive, negative, or no association between production costs and promotion costs?

6. If a studio spends $4 million on production costs, about how much money would you expect the studio to spend promoting the movie?

7. Which two movies stand out on the scatter plot you made in question 4?

8. Write a description of the information displayed by the two scatter plots.

Protein versus Fat

The following scatter plot shows the grams of fat against the grams of protein in individual servings of lunch and dinner items sold at various fast food restaurants.

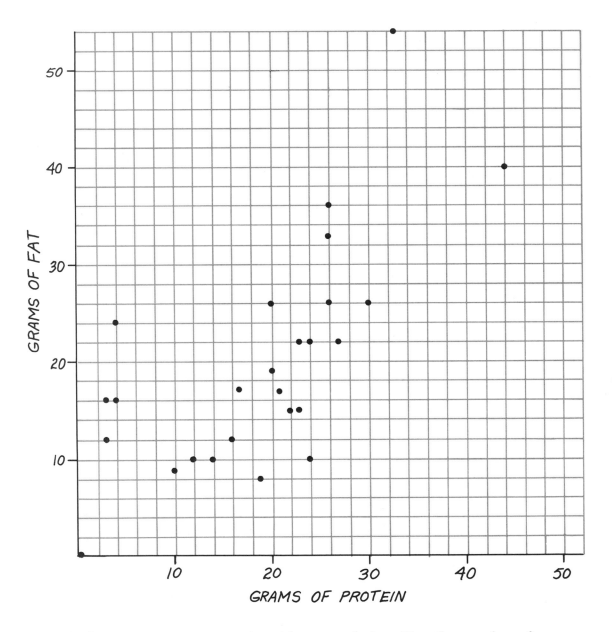

1. Suppose you want protein without much fat. Give the number of grams of protein and fat in the item that you would select.

2. What is the largest number of grams of protein in any item?

3. What is the number of grams of fat in the item in question 2?

4. Does the item in question 2 have an unusually large amount of fat considering how much protein it has?

5. What is the smallest number of grams of protein in any item?

6. How many grams of fat did the item in question 5 have?

7. Is there a positive, negative, or no association between grams of protein and grams of fat?

8. If a new item has 32 grams of protein, how many grams of fat would you expect it to have?

9. Do you see any clusters of points? Where?

The following table lists the items in the previous plot with their grams of protein and grams of fat.

	Protein grams	Fat grams
Big Mac — McDonald's	26	33
Cheeseburger — Hardee's	17	17
Double cheeseburger — Burger Chef	23	22
Cheeseburger w/Bacon Supreme — Jack-in-the-Box	33	54
Single — Wendy's	26	26
Double — Wendy's	44	40
Hamburger — McDonald's	12	10
Quarter Pounder — McDonald's	24	22
Whopper — Burger King	26	36
Roast beef — Arby's	22	15
Beef and cheese — Arby's	27	22
Roast beef — Hardee's	21	17
Big fish — Hardee's	20	26
Ham and cheese — Hardee's	23	15
Thick-crust cheese pizza — Pizza Hut	24	10
Super Supreme thin-crust pizza — Pizza Hut	30	26
Idiot's Delight pizza — Shakey's	14	10
Cheese pizza — Shakey's	16	12
Chicken McNuggets — McDonald's	20	19
Chili — Wendy's	19	8
French fries — McDonald's	3	12
Onion rings — Burger King	3	16
Chocolate shake — McDonald's	10	9
Apple turnover — Jack-in-the-Box	4	24
Chocolaty chip cookies — McDonald's	4	16
Carbonated beverages	0	0

Source: P. Hausman, *At-A-Glance Nutrition Counter*, 1984.

10. What is the item that you decided to order in question 1?

11. What kinds of items are in the cluster of question 9?

12. Do you see any single points in the scatter plot that could be outliers? That is, do you see points that don't follow the general relationship or that don't lie in a large cluster? If so, list the grams of protein and fat for those points. Which items are they? Can you give explanations for any of them?

13. With your fingers, cover up any points you identified for question 12 and the cluster from question 9, and look at the remaining points. Are they scattered fairly closely about a straight line?

14. Write a summary of the information displayed in the scatter plot.

Application 22

Walk-around Stereos

The following table lists 22 "walk-around stereos," each with its price and overall score. The overall score is based on "estimated overall quality as tape players, based on laboratory tests and judgments of features and convenience." A "perfect" walk-around stereo would have a score of 100. Consumers Union says that a difference of 7 points or less in overall score is not very significant.

Ratings of Walk-around Stereos		
Brand and Model	Price	Overall Score
AIWA HSP02	$120	73
AIWA HSJ02	180	65
JVC CQ1K	130	64
Sanyo MG100	120	64
Sony Walkman WM7	170	64
Sanyo Sportster MG16D	70	61
Toshiba KTVS1	170	60
JVC CQF2	150	59
Panasonic RQJ20X	150	59
Sharp WF9BR	140	59
Sony Walkman WM4	75	56
General Electric Stereo Escape II 35275A	90	55
KLH Solo S200	170	54
Sanyo Sportster MG36D	100	52
Koss Music Box A2	110	51
Toshiba KTS3	120	47
Panasonic RQJ75	50	46
Sears Cat. No. 21162	60	45
General Electric Great Escape 35273A	70	43
Sony Walkman WMR2	200	41
Sony Walkman WMF2	220	38
Realistic SCP4	70	37

Source: *Consumer Reports Buying Guide*, 1985.

1. Which walk-around stereo do you think is the best buy?

2. A scatter plot will give a better picture of the relative price and overall score of the walk-around stereos. Make a scatter plot with price on the horizontal axis. You can make the vertical axis as follows:

95

The ≈ lines indicate that part of the vertical axis is not shown, so that the plot is not too tall.

3. Which stereo appears to be the best buy according to the scatter plot?

4. Is there a positive, negative, or no association between price and overall score?

5. Given their overall scores, which walk-around stereos are too expensive?

Application 23

SAT Scores

The following plot shows the SAT math scores in each state in 1985 against the percentage of seniors in each state who took the test. Each state is identified by its postal code. For example, Mississippi is MS. The nationwide mean was 475.

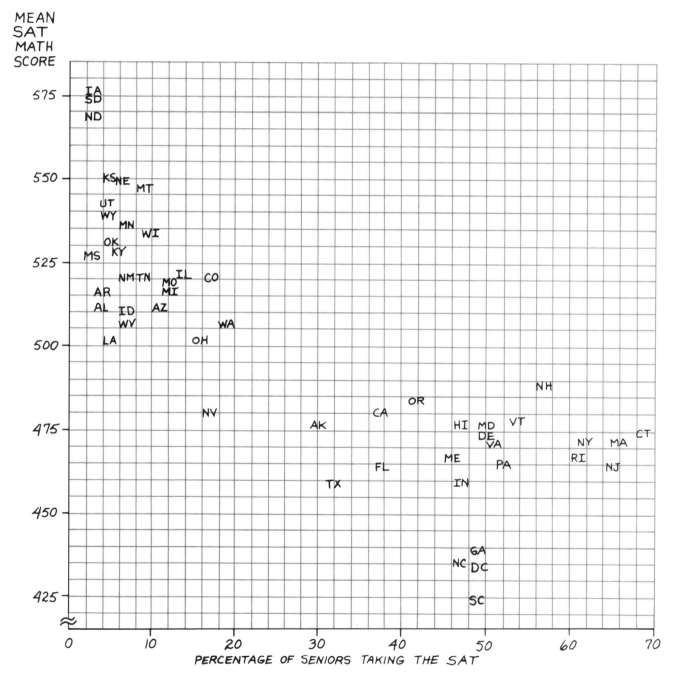

Source: The College Board.

1. In general, as a larger percentage of students take the test, what happens to the SAT math score?

2. Find the two clusters of states. Within the cluster on the left, is there a positive, negative, or no association between the percentage taking the test and the score?

3. Within the cluster on the right, is there a positive, negative, or no association?

4. Taking into account the percentage of students taking the test, which state(s) do you think have the best SAT math score? Which have the worst?

5. Using the facts you discovered in questions 1 through 4, write a summary of the information given in the scatter plot. Include an analysis of the position of your state.

Time Series Plots

Some scatter plots have year or some other time interval on the horizontal axis. Since there is only one value per year, we can connect the points in order to see the general trend. For example, the following *plot over time* shows how many 12-ounce soft drinks the average person in the U.S. drank each year from 1945 to 1984.

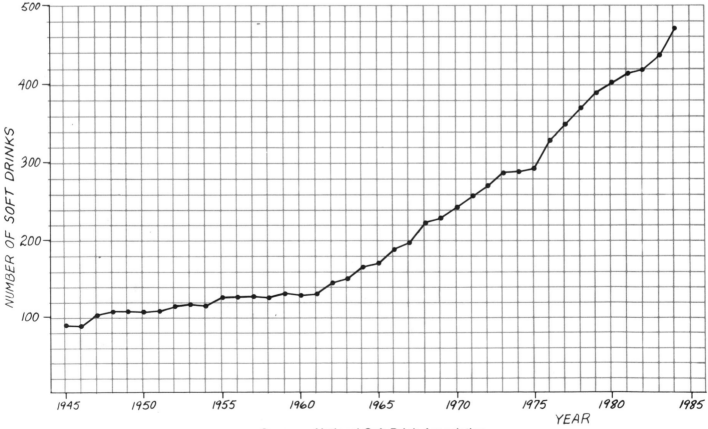

Source: National Soft Drink Association.

Discussion Questions

1. About how many soft drinks did the average person drink in 1950? In 1970?

2. About how many six-packs of soft drinks did the average person drink in 1980?

3. About how many soft drinks did the average person drink *per week* in 1950? In 1980?

4. If the trend continues, about how many 12-ounce soft drinks will the average person drink each year in 1990?

5. In what year did soft drink consumption start to "take off"? Can you think of any reason for this?

6. Who is the "average person"?

7. Write a summary of the trend in soft drink consumption shown by the plot. (Our summary of this plot follows.)

In the U.S. from 1945 until 1961, soft drink consumption rose gradually from about 90 twelve-ounce servings per year per person to about 130 twelve-ounce servings. In 1962, soft drink consumption started to rise rapidly until it was about 400 twelve-ounce servings in 1980. In other words, in these 18 years, soft drink consumption more than tripled in the United States.

What happened in 1962? Some ideas are as follows:

• Diet drinks might have been introduced.

• Soft drinks in aluminum cans might have become available.

• The economy might have improved so people started to spend more money on luxuries such as soft drinks.

• The post-war baby boom kids were reaching their teenage years.

There were very big increases in the late 70's. Then, the increase showed signs of leveling off. However, there were large increases again in 1983 and 1984.

How Long Can You Expect to Live?

1. Study the table below. At your birth, how long could you expect to live?

Life Expectancy at Birth

Birth Year	White		Black and Other	
	Male	Female	Male	Female
1920	54.4	55.6	45.5	45.2
1930	59.7	63.5	47.3	49.2
1940	62.1	66.6	51.5	54.9
1950	66.5	72.2	59.1	62.9
1955	67.4	73.7	61.4	66.1
1960	67.4	74.1	61.1	66.3
1965	67.6	74.7	61.1	67.4
1970	68.0	75.6	61.3	69.4
1971	68.3	75.8	61.6	69.7
1972	68.3	75.9	61.5	69.9
1973	68.4	76.1	61.9	70.1
1974	68.9	76.6	62.9	71.3
1975	69.4	77.2	63.6	72.3
1976	69.7	77.3	64.1	72.6
1977	70.0	77.7	64.6	73.1
1978	70.2	77.8	65.0	73.6
1979, preliminary	70.6	78.3	65.5	74.5

Source: United States National Center for Health Statistics.

2. Can males or females expect to live longer?

3. Can whites or blacks and others expect to live longer?

The life expectancies for each group have been placed on the following plot and the points have been connected by a line.

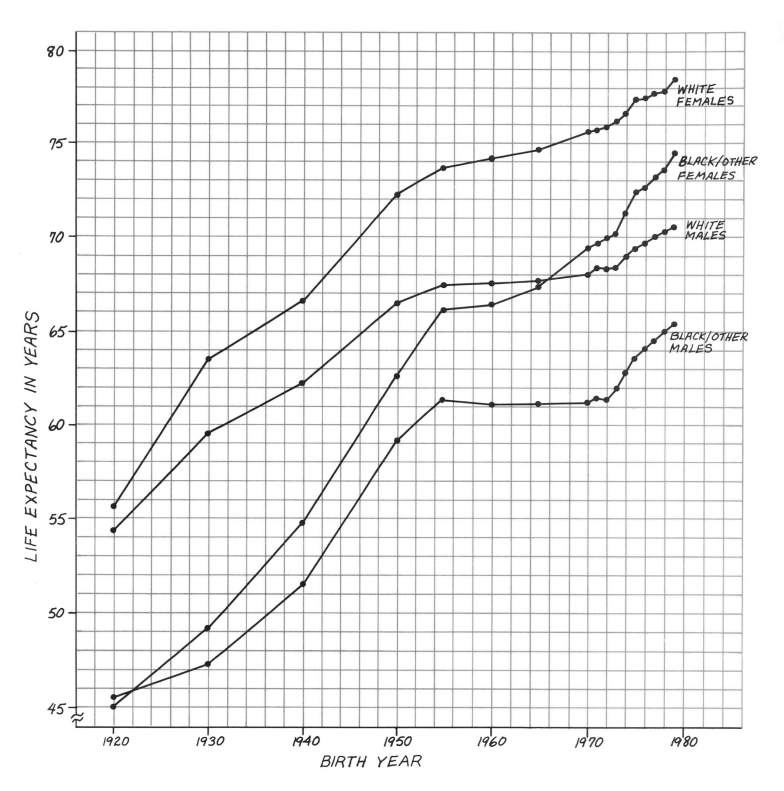

4. Which group born in 1979 could expect the longest life?

5. Which group made the greatest gain in life expectancy in the years from 1920 to 1979?

6. Which group has had the smallest increase in life expectancy since 1920?

7. During which decade did the largest increase in life expectancy occur for black and other females?

8. Within each race, males and females had about the same life expectancy in 1920. Was this still true in 1979?

9. Write a summary of the trends you see in the plot.

Application 25

Speeding

The following table shows average freeway speeds as recorded by highway monitoring devices in California. The newspaper gave no explanation why the average speed is missing for 1971 and 1973.

Year	Average Highway Speed in Miles per Hour
1970	59
1971	—
1972	61
1973	—
1974	55
1975	56
1976	57
1977	57
1978	57
1979	58
1980	56
1981	57
1982	57

Source: *Los Angeles Times*, May 22, 1983.

1. Construct a plot over time of the average speeds.

2. Can you guess what year the 55 miles per hour speed limit went into effect?

3. Some people think drivers are ignoring the 55 miles per hour speed limit. Do you think your plot shows that this is the case?

4. The fatalities in California per 100 million miles driven are shown in the following table. Construct a plot over time of these data.

Year	Fatalities per 100 Million Miles
1970	3.8
1971	3.2
1972	3.2
1973	3.0
1974	2.2
1975	2.2
1976	2.3
1977	2.4
1978	2.6
1979	2.5
1980	2.5
1981	2.4
1982	2.1

Source: *Los Angeles Times*, May 22, 1983.

5. Was there a decrease in fatalities when the 55 miles per hour speed limit took effect?

6. Another way to display these data is with a scatter plot of fatalities against speed. Construct such a plot. Place the values for speed on the horizontal axis. Plot the last two digits of the year instead of a dot.

7. What do you learn from the plot in question 6?

8. Why is the plot in question 6 the best one?

Application 26

Sex Ratio by Age

The following table gives the ratio of males to females at different ages for whites, blacks, and other races in 1980. The sex ratio is computed by dividing the number of males by the number of females.

Sex Ratio by Age (total number male/total number female)			
Age	**White**	**Black**	**Other**
0-4	1.054	1.016	1.035
5-9	1.053	1.016	1.036
10-14	1.050	1.011	1.035
15-19	1.037	.995	1.073
20-24	1.009	.913	1.087
25-29	1.003	.877	1.026
30-34	.994	.856	.971
35-39	.983	.832	.972
40-44	.974	.828	.973
45-49	.963	.821	.917
50-54	.939	.808	.878
55-59	.901	.818	.913
60-64	.869	.793	.864
65-69	.804	.745	.863
70-74	.720	.712	.925
75-79	.620	.651	.865
80-84	.524	.599	.730
85-	.429	.500	.642

Source: United States Census Bureau.

1. If there are 750 males and 500 females, what is the sex ratio?

2. If there are 500 males and 700 females, what is the sex ratio?

3. If the sex ratio is 1.000, are there more males than females, fewer males than females, or the same number of males as females?

4. If the sex ratio is 1.213, are there more males, fewer males, or the same number of males as females?

5. If the sex ratio is 0.736, are there more males, fewer males, or the same number of males as females?

6. Is there a higher percentage of males among

   a.   0-4 year old whites, 0-4 year old blacks, or 0-4 year old "others"?

   b.   80-84 year old whites, 80-84 year old blacks, or 80-84 year old "others"?

The following scatter plot shows the curves for whites, blacks, and "others."

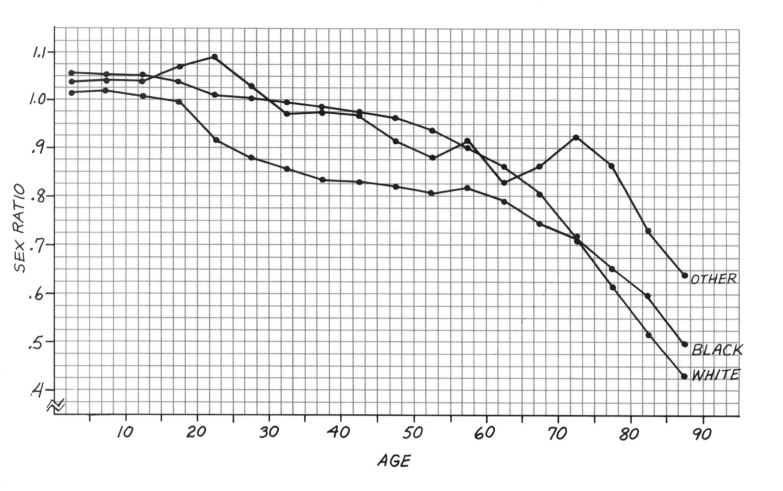

7. Do the three curves look about the same overall?

8. What is one general characteristic of all three curves?

9. What does it mean when the curve is going downhill?

10. Where are the curves closest?

11. a) At what ages do the curves for whites and blacks first start separating?

    b) Can you think of any possible explanations for this?

12. a) How do the white and black curves compare at older ages?

    b) Again, can you think of any possible explanations for this?

13. Write a description of the information you see in this plot. Include any questions the plot suggests to you.

Scatter Plots — Summary

Scatter plots are the best way to display data in which two numbers are given for each person or item. When you analyze a scatter plot, look for the following:

- positive, negative, or no association
- clusters of points
- points that do not follow the general pattern

If you find any of these features, ask yourself what could have caused them.

On time series plots, it is often helpful to connect the points in order to see the trend. Look for places where the general trend seems to change, and try to find possible explanations. If there is more than one time series on a plot, compare them to determine similarities and differences.

Suggestions for Student Projects

Think of a problem that interests you or select one of those below. Collect the data, make the appropriate plot(s), and write a summary of your results. Try to explain any trends or patterns.

1. Did the students who studied the most hours tend to get the higher grades on your last test?

2. Do students who get the most allowance tend to work more hours doing chores at home?

3. Can the students who do the most sit-ups in one minute also do the most push-ups?

4. Investigate whether there are relationships between certain physical characteristics by measuring a group of students. Some possibilities include the following:

   a. height and elbow-hand length

   b. circumference of closed fist and length of foot

   c. hand span and circumference of wrist

   d. weight and waist

   e. circumferences of head and neck

5. Construct a plot over time of the number of absences in your class on each day of the last six weeks. What trends do you see?

VII. LINES ON SCATTER PLOTS

The 45° Line

In the last section we interpreted scatter plots by looking for general relationships of positive, negative, and no association. We also looked for clusters of points that seemed special in some way. This section shows how interpretations of scatter plots are sometimes helped by adding a straight line to the plot. Two different straight lines are used. One is the 45° line going through the points (0, 0), (1, 1), (2, 2), and so forth. The second type is a straight line that is fitted to go through much of the data.

This table lists the number of black state legislators for each state in 1974 and 1984.

Number of Black State Legislators					
	1974	1984		1974	1984
Alabama	3	24	Montana	0	0
Alaska	2	1	Nebraska	1	1
Arizona	2	2	Nevada	3	3
Arkansas	4	5	New Hampshire	0	0
California	7	8	New Jersey	7	7
Colorado	4	3	New Mexico	1	0
Connecticut	6	10	New York	14	20
Delaware	3	3	North Carolina	3	15
District of Columbia	n/a	n/a	North Dakota	0	0
Florida	3	12	Ohio	11	12
Georgia	16	26	Oklahoma	4	5
Hawaii	0	0	Oregon	1	3
Idaho	0	0	Pennsylvania	13	18
Illinois	19	20	Rhode Island	1	4
Indiana	7	8	South Carolina	3	20
Iowa	1	1	South Dakota	0	0
Kansas	5	4	Tennessee	9	13
Kentucky	3	2	Texas	8	13
Louisiana	8	18	Utah	0	1
Maine	1	0	Vermont	0	1
Maryland	19	24	Virginia	2	7
Massachusetts	5	6	Washington	2	3
Michigan	13	17	West Virginia	1	1
Minnesota	2	1	Wisconsin	3	4
Mississippi	1	20	Wyoming	0	1
Missouri	15	15	Total	236	382

Source: Joint Center for Political Studies.

The scatter plot of the 1984 number against the 1974 number follows:

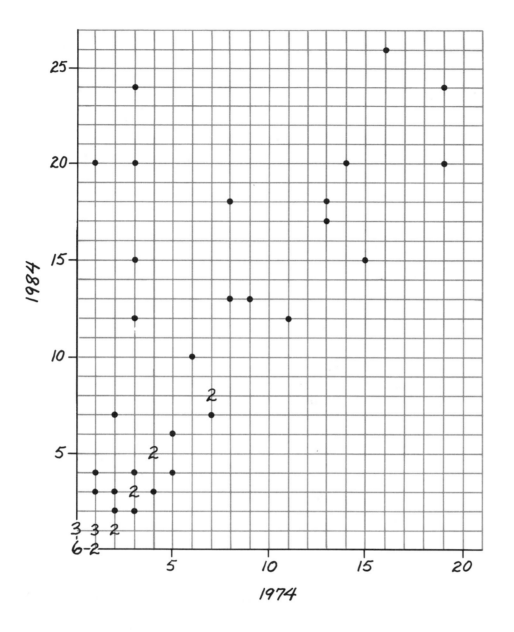

A striking feature of the plot is that the points all seem to lie above an (imaginary) diagonal line. Another feature is that there are many points in the lower left-hand corner. In fact, several states sometimes lie at exactly the same point. For example, Arkansas and Oklahoma both lie at (4, 5). To show this, we placed a 2 at (4, 5).

Discussion Questions

1. Place a ruler on the plot next to the line going through (0, 0), (10, 10), (20, 20), and so forth. For states on this line, the 1984 and 1974 numbers of black legislators are equal. How many points are exactly on this line?

2. If a point is above this line, the number of black legislators in that state in 1984 is larger than the number of black legislators that state had in 1974. Name three states for which this statement is true.

3. How many points fall below this line? What can we say about these states? What is the maximum (vertical) distance any of these is below the line? What does this mean in terms of the number of black legislators in 1974 and 1984?

4. Again, consider states above this line, those where the number of black legislators was larger in 1984 than in 1974. What are the names of the 7 or so states that lie farthest above the line? What do these states have in common?

5. The number of black legislators has generally increased from 1974 to 1984. Does this mean that the percentage of legislators who are black has necessarily increased? (Hint: Is the total number of legislators in a state necessarily the same in 1984 as in 1974?)

In summary, this 45° line (sometimes called the $y = x$ line) divides the plot into two regions. We should try to distinguish the characteristics of the points in the two regions. In this plot the top region contains states where the number of black legislators in 1984 is larger than it was in 1974. Most of the states lie in this region. The points in this region that are farthest from the line are those where the number has increased the most from 1974 to 1984. These states turn out to be states in the deep south. There are only a few points slightly below the 45° line, where the number of black legislators was greater in 1974 than in 1984. These are all states that had only 5 or fewer black legislators in 1974. Almost half the states are in the lower left-hand corner, with 5 or fewer in both years. Two states, Illinois and Maryland, had relatively large numbers in both years.

It would have been helpful to plot each state's abbreviation (such as NY for New York) instead of a dot. However, there wasn't room to do this for the states in the lower left corner.

Application 27

Submarine Sinkings

During World War II, the United States Navy tried to estimate how many German submarines were sunk each month. After the war, the Navy was able to get the actual numbers. The results follow:

Month	U.S. Estimate	Actual Number of Sinkings
1	3	3
2	2	2
3	4	6
4	2	3
5	5	4
6	5	3
7	9	11
8	12	9
9	8	10
10	13	16
11	14	13
12	3	5
13	4	6
14	13	19
15	10	15
16	16	15

Source: Mosteller, Fienberg, and Rourke, *Beginning Statistics with Data Analysis.*

1. Make a scatter plot of the data. Put the U.S. estimate on the horizontal axis.

2. Draw in the line that connects all the points where the number estimated by the U.S. Navy would be the same as the actual number of sinkings.

3. If a point is above the line, does it mean that the U.S. Navy's estimate was too high or too low?

4. Are more points above the line or below it?

5. Did the U.S. Navy tend to underestimate or overestimate the number of submarine sinkings?

6. Which point is farthest from the line? How many units away from the line is it? (Count the units vertically from the point to the line.)

7. How many points are three units or more from the line?

Fitting a Line

Not all ducks look alike, and it turns out that not all species of ducks behave alike, either. In an effort to study possible relationships between looks and behavior of ducks, two scales were created and an experiment performed. A plumage scale was devised to reflect the color and other characteristics of the duck's feathers. The scale ranged from 0 (looks just like a mallard with a green head and white neck-ring) to 20 (looks just like a pintail with a needle tail and neck stripe). Similarly, a behavior scale was devised ranging from 0 (generally congregate in pairs, just like mallards) to 15 (generally congregate in larger groups, just like pintails). The crucial scientific question is: After some interbreeding of mallards and pintails to produce ducks with a variety of looks and behavior, will we be able to predict how the ducks behave from their looks?

An experiment was performed. Mallards were mated with pintails and 11 second generation males were studied. For ease of identification, we have named the ducks. The results follow:

Duck	Plumage	Behavior
Rub	7	3
Stu	13	10
Ugly	14	11
Fred	6	5
Y.U.	14	15
Kold	15	15
Don	4	7
Ole	8	10
Van	7	4
Joe	9	9
Lou	14	11

Source: Richard J. Larsen and Donna Fox Stroup, *Statistics in the Real World.*

Kold Duck looked the most like a pintail. Don Duck looked the most like a mallard. The scatter plot of these data follows:

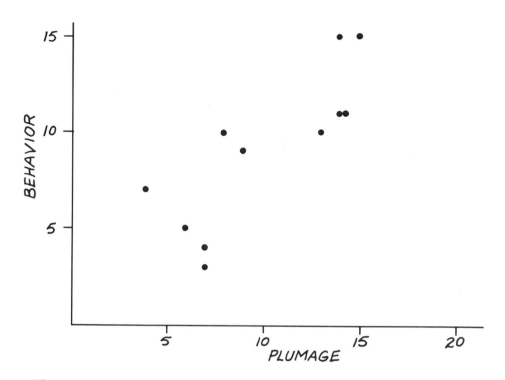

There is a positive association between a duck's plumage rating and his behavior rating. Ducks who look more like pintails tend to act more like pintails.

The same plot with a line through the points follows. This line is called the *fitted line*.

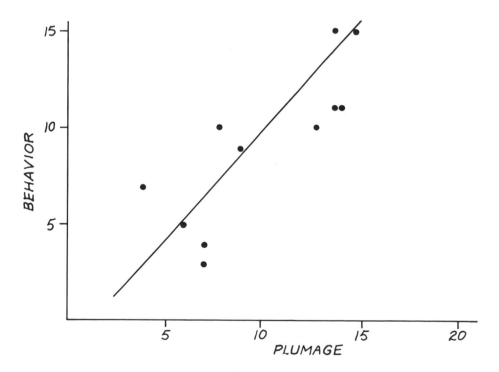

We can use this line to predict the behavior rating of a duck with a given plumage rating. For example, if a duck has a plumage rating of 5, what would you expect for his behavior rating?

113

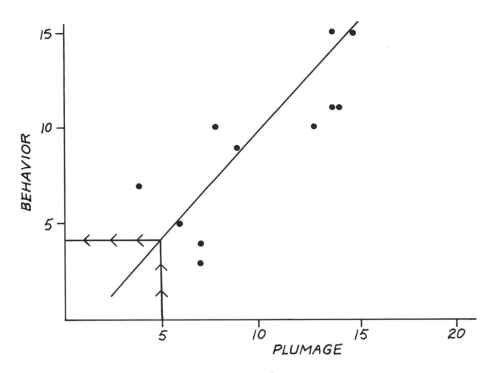

You should expect a behavior rating of 4.

Now we will describe a method for drawing a line through the data in order to predict a duck's behavior rating if we are given a plumage rating.

First, count the total number of points. Draw two vertical dashed lines so there are approximately the same number of points in each of the three strips. The two outer strips should have the same number of points, if possible.

In this case, we have 11 points. We will have four points in each outside strip and three points in the middle.

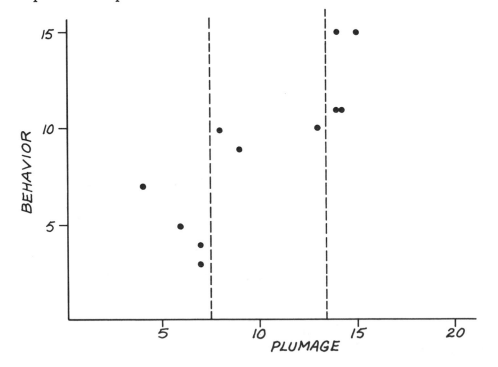

Second, place an X in each strip at the "center" of the points in that strip.

Study the left strip. It has four points. We want to find the median of the plumage ratings and the median of the behavior ratings. The median of the plumage ratings is halfway between the second and third points counting from the left. To find the median of the plumage ratings, place a ruler to the left of the points and move it toward the right until it is halfway between the second and third points. Draw a short vertical dashed line there.

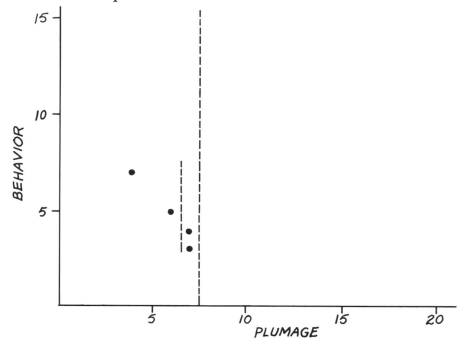

The median of the behavior ratings is halfway between the second and third points, counting from the bottom. Move the ruler up until it is halfway between these points and draw a horizontal dashed line there. The plot is shown as follows:

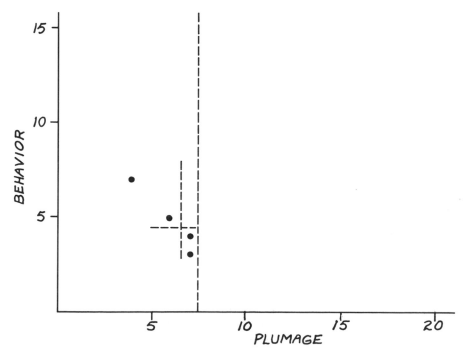

Mark an X where the dashed lines cross.

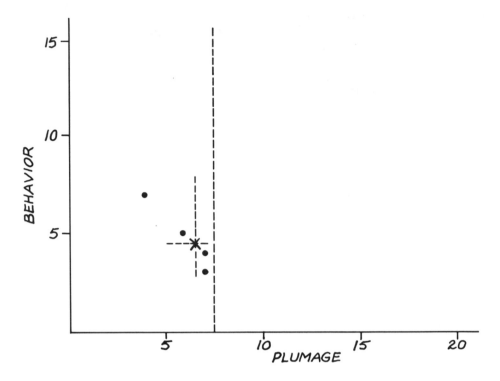

The center strip has three points. The median of the plumage ratings is at the second point, counting from the left.

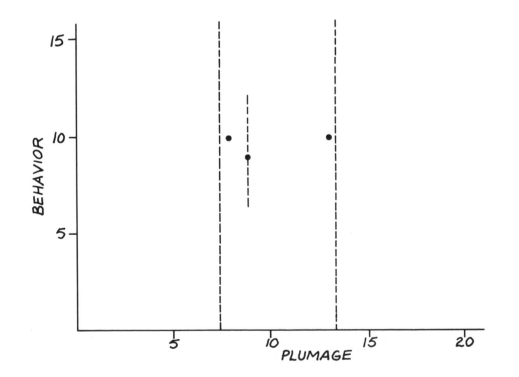

The median of the behavior ratings is at the second point, counting from the bottom.

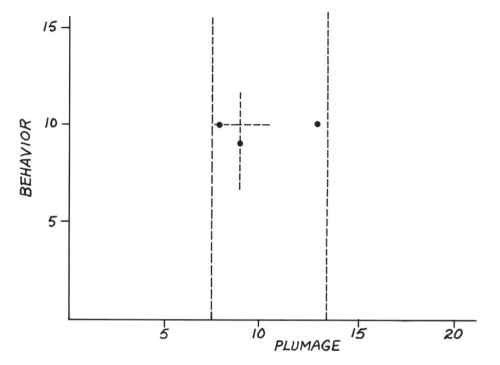

Mark an X where the dashed lines cross.

After the "center" of the right strip is also found, the plot looks as follows:

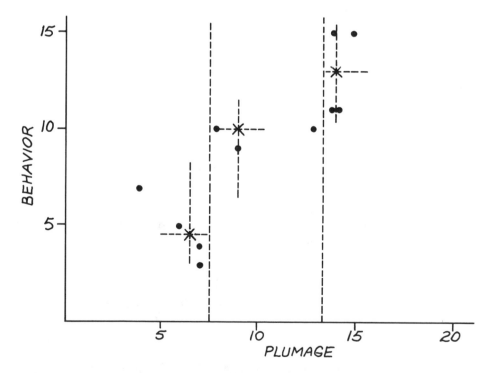

The third step is to decide whether or not the three X's lie close to a straight line. Use your ruler, balanced on its edge, to help decide. For this example, the X's lie approximately on a straight line.

Finally, place your ruler so that it connects the two *X*'s in the outside strips. Now slide the ruler one-third of the way to the middle *X* and draw the line.

The finished plot including the fitted line is shown below. It is not necessary to include the dashed lines.

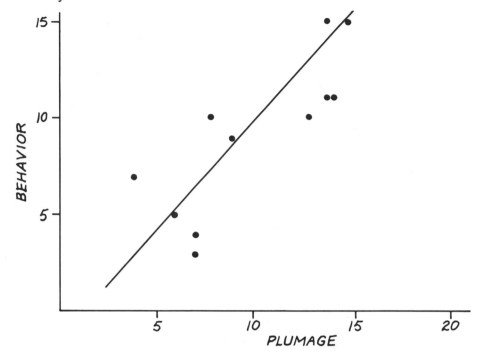

Discussion Questions

1. Which duck behaved the most like a pintail?

2. Which duck behaved the most like a mallard?

3. Why do we need a method for drawing a line? Why can't we just sketch one?

4. If a duck has a plumage rating of 10, what would you expect his behavior rating to be? Use the fitted line to get your answer.

5. If a duck has a plumage rating of 4, what would you expect his behavior rating to be?

6. To judge how much a duck's actual behavior differs from its predicted behavior, we measure the vertical distance from the point to the fitted line. Which duck is farthest from the line, and how many units is he from the line?

7. Which ducks are within two units of the line?

8. You might wonder why the fitted line has been constructed this way. Why have we used medians instead of means to form the *X*'s? Why have we constructed three *X*'s instead of two or four? Why have we constructed the slope of the line by using only the two end *X*'s? After connecting the two end *X*'s, why did we slide the ruler one-third of the way towards the middle *X* rather than some other fraction? Try to think of reasons for these choices or of alternate reasons for constructing a fitted line in a different way.

Application 28

Smoking and Heart Disease

The following table lists 21 countries with the cigarette consumption per adult per year and the number of deaths per 100,000 people per year from coronary heart disease (CHD).

Country	Cigarette Consumption per Adult per Year	CHD Mortality per 100,000 (ages 35-64)
United States	3900	257
Canada	3350	212
Australia	3220	238
New Zealand	3220	212
United Kingdom	2790	194
Switzerland	2780	125
Ireland	2770	187
Iceland	2290	111
Finland	2160	233
West Germany	1890	150
Netherlands	1810	125
Greece	1800	41
Austria	1770	182
Belgium	1700	118
Mexico	1680	32
Italy	1510	114
Denmark	1500	145
France	1410	60
Sweden	1270	127
Spain	1200	44
Norway	1090	136

Source: *American Journal of Public Health.*

1. In which country do adults smoke the largest number of cigarettes?
2. Which country has the highest death rate from coronary heart disease?
3. Which country has the lowest death rate from coronary heart disease?
4. If we want to predict CHD mortality from cigarette consumption, which variable should be placed on the horizontal axis of a scatter plot?
5. a) Make a scatter plot of the data.
   b) Draw two vertical lines so there are seven points in each strip.
   c) Place an X in each strip at the median of the cigarette consumption and the median of the CHD mortality.
   d) Do the three X's lie close to a straight line?
   e) Draw in the fitted line.

6. a) Which three countries lie the farthest vertical distance from the line?

   b) How many units do they lie from the line?

   c) Considering the cigarette consumption, are these countries relatively high or low in CHD mortality?

7. If you were told that the adults in a country smoke an average of 2500 cigarettes a year, how many deaths from CHD would you expect?

8. If you were told that the adults in a country smoke an average of 1300 cigarettes a year, how many deaths from CHD would you expect?

9. (For class discussion) Sometimes strong association in a scatter plot is taken to mean that one of the variables *causes* the other one. Do you think that a high CHD death rate could cause cigarette consumption to be high? Could high cigarette consumption cause the CHD death rate to be high? Sometimes, though, there is not a causal relationship between the two variables. Instead, there is a hidden third variable. This variable could cause both of the variables to be large simultaneously. Do you think that this might be the situation for this example? Can you think of such a possible variable?

10. (For students who have studied algebra.) Choose two points on the fitted line, and from them find the equation of the line. Express it in the form $y = mx + b$, where y is mortality from coronary heart disease per 100,000 people (aged 35-64) per year, and x is cigarette consumption per adult per year. Using this equation, how many additional deaths per 100,000 people tend to result from an increase of 200 in cigarette consumption? What number of cigarettes per year is associated with one additional death from CHD per 100,000 people per year?

Application 29

Catholic Clergy

Nineteen states have more than 500,000 residents who are Catholic. The following table lists these states, along with the number of priests and nuns in each state.

| State | Number of | |
	Priests	Nuns
Arizona	412	591
California	4242	6615
Connecticut	1298	2450
Florida	1224	1240
Illinois	4131	8564
Indiana	1229	2515
Iowa	982	2140
Louisiana	1236	1931
Massachusetts	3630	6715
Michigan	1892	4296
Minnesota	1403	3911
Missouri	1660	4049
New Jersey	2784	5102
New York	7334	14665
Ohio	2901	6685
Pennsylvania	4600	12785
Rhode Island	580	1105
Texas	2146	3832
Wisconsin	2167	5176

Source: *The Official Catholic Directory.*

Clearly, the number of priests and nuns varies greatly among these states. This application investigates whether there is any relationship between the number of priests and the number of nuns.

1. Make a scatter plot of the number of nuns on the vertical axis against the number of priests on the horizontal axis.

2. Fit a straight line to the scatter plot.

3. Do you feel that a straight line fits these data well, overall?

4. New York is the state with the largest number of Catholic clergy. Would you say that the two numbers for New York follow the same relationship as do the other states? Give your reasons.

5. Which state has a large number of nuns compared to its number of priests? Which state has a relatively small number of nuns compared to its number of priests?

6. (For students who have studied algebra.) Find the equation of the fitted line. Express it in the form $y = mx + b$, where y is the number of nuns and x is the number of priests. According to this equation, if one state had 100 more priests than a second state, how many more nuns would we expect the first state to have than the second? If there were 100 priests in a state, how many nuns would the equation predict? The moral is: One should be careful using fitted lines for values far to the left or right of the given points.

Application 30

Voting for President

The following table gives the percentage of the vote received by the Democratic candidate in the presidential elections of 1920, 1960, and 1964. The percentages were calculated using only votes for the two major party candidates. The question we want to investigate here is whether the 1964 percentage can be predicted from either the 1920 or the 1960 percentage. Only states in the northeast and midwest are included.

| | Percentage Vote Received by Democrat | | |
State	1920	1960	1964
Colorado	38	45	62
Connecticut	35	54	68
Delaware	43	51	61
Illinois	27	50	59
Indiana	42	45	56
Iowa	26	43	62
Kansas	33	39	55
Maine	30	43	69
Maryland	43	54	66
Massachusetts	29	60	76
Michigan	23	51	67
Minnesota	22	51	64
Nebraska	33	38	53
New Hampshire	40	47	64
New Jersey	30	50	66
New York	29	53	69
North Dakota	19	45	58
Ohio	40	47	63
Pennsylvania	29	51	65
Rhode Island	34	64	81
South Dakota	24	42	56
Vermont	24	41	66
West Virginia	44	53	68
Wisconsin	18	48	62

Source: United States Census Bureau.

1. By looking down the columns of percentages, do you think the Democratic or Republican candidate won the election in

   a. 1920?

   b. 1960?

   c. 1964?

SECTION VII: LINES ON SCATTER PLOTS

2. Make a scatter plot with the 1960 percentages on the horizontal axis and the 1964 percentages on the vertical axis.

3. Is there a positive, negative, or no association? Why?

4. Fit a straight line to the scatter plot. Due to the fact that three states have a 1960 percentage of 45 and four states have a 1960 percentage of 51, you will have to have 9 states in the left group, 5 in the middle group, and 10 in the right group.

5. Which two states lie the farthest vertical distance from the line?

6. Use your line to complete these sentences.

   a. A state with a 50% vote for the Democratic candidate in 1960 would give the Democratic candidate about a _____% vote in 1964.

   b. A state with a 60% vote for the Democratic candidate in 1960 would give the Democratic candidate about a _____% vote in 1964.

   c. As an approximation using the fitted line, the 1964 vote can be estimated by adding about _____% to the 1960 vote.

7. We call the vertical distance of each point from the fitted line the "error." With the exception of the two states in question 5, all the rest of the states give an "error" less than _____.

8. Putting together the information in questions 5, 6, and 7, we can say the following: The 1964 Democratic percentage equals the 1960 Democratic percentage plus _____%, with an error of less than _____% for all these states except for two, which are _____ and _____.

9. Now make a scatter plot with the 1920 percentages on the horizontal axis and the 1964 percentages on the vertical axis.

10. Is there positive, negative, or no association? Why?

11. Divide the plot into three vertical strips and mark the X in each strip. The three X's do not lie close to a straight line, so do not draw one in.

12. Is it possible to predict the 1964 vote if you are given the 1920 vote?

13. Summarize the information from these two scatter plots in a paragraph.

14. What two candidates ran in

    a. 1920?

    b. 1960?

    c. 1964?

Fitting a Line with a More Complicated Example

When the scatter plot has more points on it than in the previous examples, we can still use the method that was described to fit a straight line. However, some parts of the construction and interpretation can be more complicated, so we will now work a larger example.

The following scatter plot shows the weights and heights of 52 men in an office. Notice that in several places there is a 2 in the plot. This means that two men had the same height and weight.

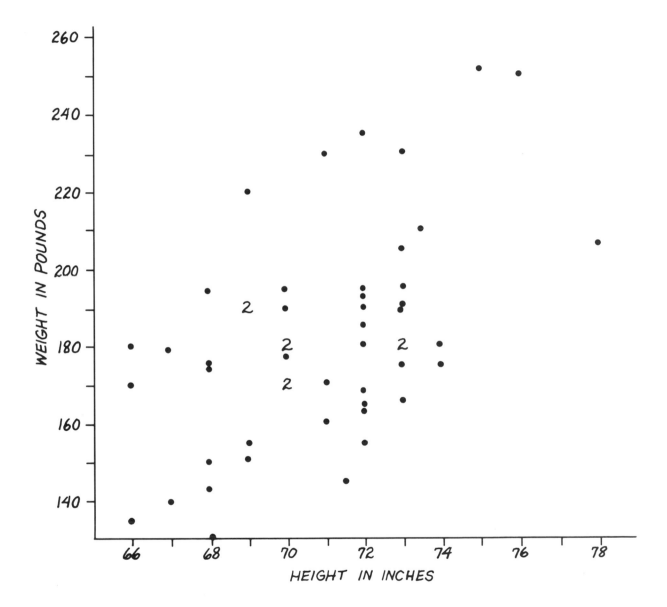

There are 52 points, so to construct the fitted line we would like to divide the points into groups of 17, 18, and 17 points. This division is not possible because different men have the same height. For example, for the left group there are 16 men with heights 69" or less, and 23 men with heights 70" or less. We cannot construct a group with exactly 17 men, so we choose the group with 16 by making the dividing line at 69.5". For the right group, counting in from the right side of the plot shows that 15 men have heights

73" or taller, and 25 men have heights 72" or taller. Similarly, we choose the dividing point to be 72.5", so the right group has 15 points. This choice leaves 21 points in the middle. The dividing lines are shown in the following scatter plot.

Next, we find the centers of the three groups, using the median method. For the left group of 16 points, both the eighth and ninth largest heights are 68", so the median height is 68". For the weights, the eighth largest is 170 and the ninth is 175, so the median weight is 172.5 pounds. These medians give the left X on the scatter plot. For the right group of 15 points, the eighth height is 73" and the eighth weight is 190 pounds. These medians give the right X on the plot. Similarly, the center X is obtained from the 21 points in the center group as before.

The scatter plot with the three X's follows. It is important to stop now and see if the three X's fall reasonably close to a straight line. If they do not, we would not continue to fit the straight line.

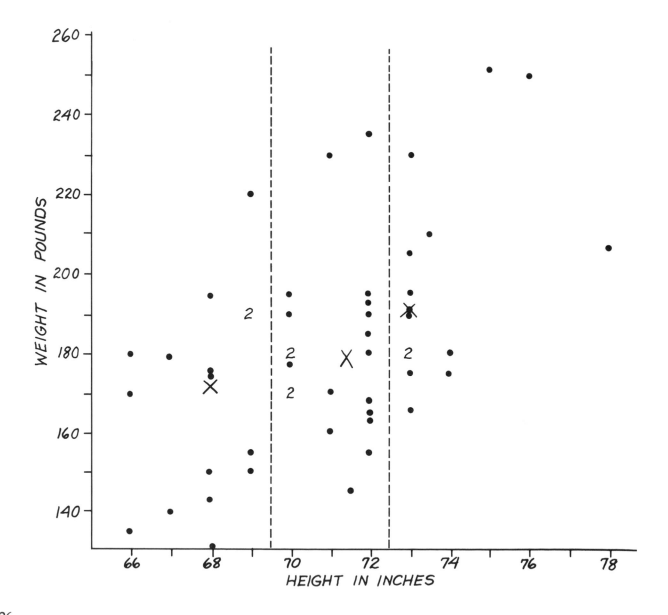

In this case the three X's are close to a straight line, so we continue. Draw the fitted line by first taking a straightedge and placing it along the two end X's. The middle X is below this line. We now slide the straightedge down one-third of the way towards the middle X and draw in the fitted line. This line is shown in the following scatter plot.

The fitted line does not go exactly through any of the three X's, but it goes close to each of them. From this straight line we can predict that a typical weight for a man 66″ tall is 160 pounds, and a typical weight for a man 76″ tall is 197 pounds. For a 10″ increase in height there is a typical increase in weight of 37 pounds, so we could say that on the average for each one inch increase in height there is a 3.7 pound increase in weight. It would be difficult to draw a conclusion like this without fitting a line to the scatter plot.

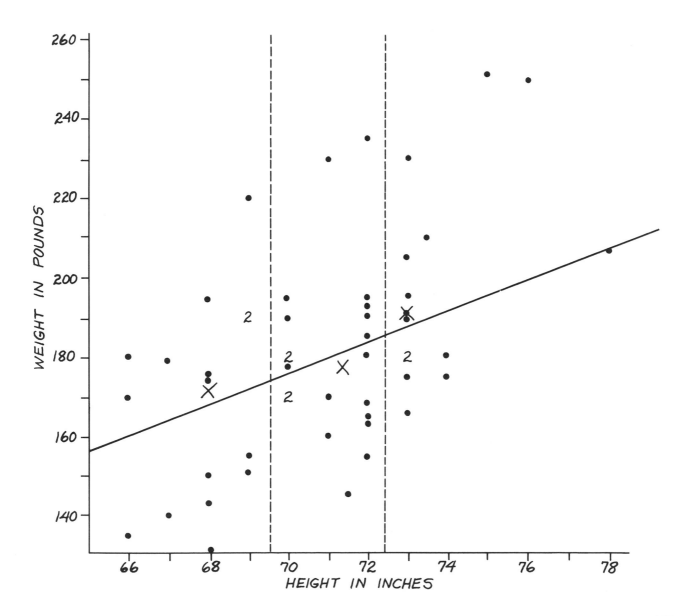

It is also useful to examine the spread of the points about the fitted line. A good way to do this is to add two additional lines that are parallel to the fitted line. We want these new lines to be an equal distance above and below the fitted line. We also want them drawn far enough from the fitted line so that most, but not all, of the points lie between the two new lines. This lets us notice and focus our attention more easily on outlying points or on other unusual features of the data around the edges.

This has been done in the following plot, using lines giving weights that are 30 pounds more, and 30 pounds less, than the predicted weight for each height. The value 30 pounds was chosen by sliding a ruler parallel to the fitted line so that most, but not all, of the men would fall between these additional lines.

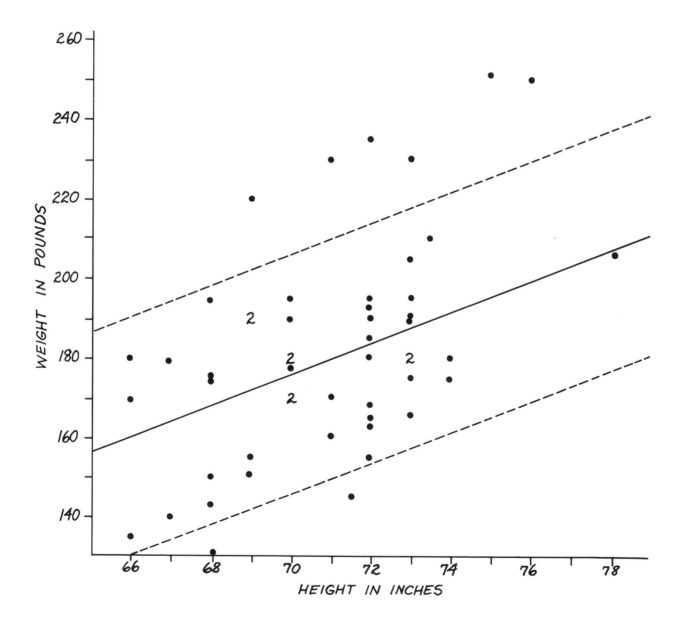

Discussion Questions

1. How many men fall above the top line? Below the bottom line?

2. What percentage of these 52 men would you say are unusually heavy for their height (above the top line)?

3. What percentage of these 52 men would you say are unusually light for their height?

4. Are there more men who are very heavy for their height, or are there more men who are very light for their height? Why do you think this is the case?

5. For those men whose weight is unusually heavy or unusually light for their height, which group has the more extreme values of weight?

6. Consider the man with height 78".

   a. How many men are heavier than he is?

   b. Do you think he is overweight? Why or why not?

1980-84 Rock Hits

The following table lists the top 25 single records from 1980 through 1984 and the number of weeks each of these was in the Top 10 and the Top 40. Is there a close relationship between these two numbers? If we know how many weeks a hit record was in the Top 10, could we accurately predict the total length of time it would remain in the Top 40?

Top Record Hits, 1980-1984

Title — Artist	Number of weeks in	
	Top 10	Top 40
"Physical" — Olivia Newton-John	15	21
"Endless Love" — Diana Ross & Lionel Richie	13	19
"Bette Davis Eyes" — Kim Carnes	14	20
"Every Breath You Take" — Police	13	20
"Billie Jean" — Michael Jackson	11	17
"I Love Rock 'n Roll" — Joan Jett & The Blackhearts	12	16
"Ebony and Ivory" — Paul McCartney & Stevie Wonder	12	15
"Flashdance ... What a Feeling" — Irene Cara	14	20
"Centerfold" — J. Geils Band	12	20
"Lady" — Kenny Rogers	13	19
"Call Me" — Blondie	12	19
"Eye of the Tiger" — Survivor	15	18
"Say Say Say" — Paul McCartney & Michael Jackson	13	18
"(Just Like) Starting Over" — John Lennon	14	19
"When Doves Cry" — Prince	11	16
"Jump" — Van Halen	10	15
"Total Eclipse of the Heart" — Bonnie Tyler	11	18
"Upside Down" — Diana Ross	14	17
"Another Brick in the Wall (part II)" — Pink Floyd	12	19
"Down Under" — Men At Work	10	19
"Rock with You" — Michael Jackson	9	19
"All Night Long (All Night)" — Lionel Richie	13	17
"Maneater" — Daryl Hall & John Oates	13	17
"Magic" — Olivia Newton-John	9	16
"Funkytown" — Lipps, Inc.	9	15

Source: *The Billboard Book of Top 40 Hits*, 1985.

1. Construct a scatter plot, putting weeks in the Top 40 on the vertical axis and weeks in the Top 10 on the horizontal axis.

2. Next divide the data into three groups. There are 25 points, so we would like to have three groups of 8, 9, and 8 points. However, notice that there are many records that are tied with the same Top 10 values.

For the right group, if we include records 14 or more weeks in the Top 10, we would have 6 points. If we include records 13 or more weeks in the Top 10, we would have 12 points. In order to have enough points remaining to put into the other two groups, it seems reasonable to make the right group consist of the 6 records with 14 or more weeks in the Top 10. Decide how to form the left and center groups.

3. Using these three groups, fit the line to these data.

4. If a record stayed in the Top 10 for ten weeks, about how long would it stay in the Top 40?

5. Which records are farthest from the line? Did they spend a relatively long or short time in the Top 40 compared to their time in the Top 10? Can you think of any reasons?

6. Write a paragraph that summarizes these data.

52 Men in an Insurance Office

The following table lists the heights, shoe sizes, and weights for 52 men in an office. These weights and heights were discussed earlier, on pages 125 to 129. Now we will consider shoe size against height to see if this relationship is similar to or different from the relationship with weight and height.

Height	Shoe Size	Weight	Height	Shoe Size	Weight
70	10.5	195	73	10	190
68	10.5	195	70	9.5	180
69	8.5	152	72	9	168
72	10.5	185	72	10	193
72	10	180	74	12	175
73	9.5	189	71	9	160
74	11	180	72	9.5	163
70	10	180	73	10.5	175
72	9.5	155	72	10	235
73	11	180	71	12	230
68	7	150	69	9.5	220
72	10	195	75	12	252
66	7	135	68	10	175
67	8.5	178	76	13	250
68	9	143	69	9	190
69	10	190	70	10	170
70	9.5	170	73	10	230
73	10.5	205	73	11.5	195
73	10	180	72	9.5	190
67	8.5	140	66	8.5	170
72	10	165	68	8.5	130
70	10	190	73	10.5	166
70	9.5	178	78	13	207
73.5	11	210	66	8.5	180
71.5	10	145	71	9	170
68	9	176	69	9	155

1. Construct a scatter plot of shoe size against height. Put height on the horizontal axis. There are several men with exactly the same height and shoe size. For example, 5 men have the same height of 72" and the same shoe size of 10, so there should be a 5 at that position on the plot. At first, you will want to make the scatter plot lightly with pencil so you can change the dots to numerals as necessary.

2. Use the method that was given to fit a line to these points. (Since there are many repeated heights on the horizontal axis, you will want the three groups to have 16, 21, and 15 points, from left to right.) Does the line fit well?

3. What shoe size would you predict for a man 66" tall? For a man 76" tall? About how many additional inches of height are needed for a man's predicted shoe size to increase by one whole size?

4. Draw lines 1-1/2 shoe sizes above and 1-1/2 shoe sizes below the fitted line. Are there many points falling outside this range? Are they primarily above the top line or below the bottom line?

5. Are there any outlying points in the plot that do not follow the relationship given by the fitted line?

6. Compare the plot of shoe size against height with the earlier plot of weight against height. Which plot indicates a closer, tighter relationship? Does this surprise you? Can you think of any explanation for this?

Fitted Straight Lines — Clustering and Curvature

In the previous section there were many scatter plots that can be appropriately fitted with straight lines. However, don't assume that it is always appropriate to fit a straight line to a scatter plot. Sometimes the points simply do not lie near a single straight line. Two possibilities are that the data could be *clustered* into two or more groups in the scatter plot or that the data might fall near a *curved* (not straight) line.

How can we tell if there is clustering or curvature, and what should we do about them? Look at the scatter plot as a whole, as you did in Section VI, to see if you observe clusters or a curved relationship. Sometimes clusters or curvature are more obvious after a straight line has been fitted. Always look at a plot again after fitting a line to see if something is apparent that wasn't before.

In some cases, a straight line fits well within one of the clusters but not to all the data. Then you can use this line for prediction or summary within the range of data corresponding to the cluster, but don't use a single line that is fitted to all the data. Sometimes you might fit two separate straight lines to different parts of the data. These lines can help you see that a single straight line does not fit well and that a curve might be better. Of course, you might decide instead that no straight or curved line fits well and none should be used for prediction or summary. This could be the best answer.

The following two applications have scatter plots containing clustering and curvature. For these plots it is best not to interpret the data in terms of a single straight line fit.

Telephone Office Costs (Clustering)

The following scatter plot involves some engineering data. The horizontal axis gives the number of telephone lines that can be handled by each of 20 telephone switching offices. (A telephone switching office is the place that local telephone calls pass through and one customer is connected to another.) The vertical axis gives an estimate of the total cost of constructing the office. The cost depends on more than just the number of telephone lines. Each point in the scatter plot represents one telephone switching office. The horizontal value is the number of telephone lines into the office and the vertical value is the total cost. We want to study the scatter plot to learn whether or not there is a close relationship between cost and capacity for these switching offices.

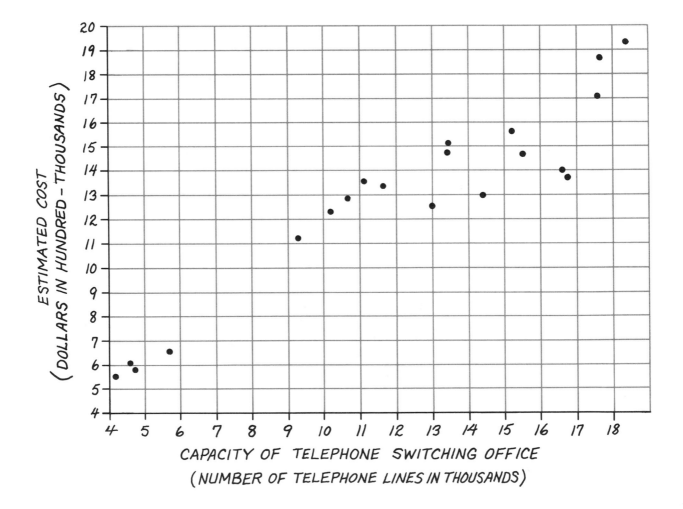

The first general impression is that there is a large gap in the data, giving two separate groups of switching offices. The bottom four offices are all separated by over 3,000 lines from the smallest of the other 16. You might think that the topmost three points should also be treated as a separate cluster. Perhaps they should be, but the gap on the horizontal axis here is definitely smaller, only about 1,000 lines. Thus, as a first step, it seems sensible to treat the data as two clusters rather than one or three.

The data values for the 20 offices are listed in the following table. You will need to construct or trace a scatter plot such as the preceding one to answer the following questions.

Switching Office Capacity (lines)	Estimated Cost	Switching Office Capacity (lines)	Estimated Cost
4,200	$560,000	13,200	$1,470,000
4,600	610,000	13,300	1,510,000
4,700	580,000	14,400	1,300,000
5,700	660,000	15,200	1,580,000
9,300	1,120,000	15,500	1,480,000
10,200	1,230,000	16,700	1,400,000
10,700	1,270,000	16,800	1,370,000
11,100	1,360,000	17,600	1,710,000
11,600	1,340,000	17,700	1,870,000
13,000	1,250,000	18,400	1,930,000

1. For an office with 5,000 telephone lines, what cost would you estimate? Do not fit any straight line. Just scan the plot to get an estimate.

2. Fit a straight line to the cluster of 16 larger offices.

3. For offices of about 18,000 telephone lines, what cost does this line predict?

4. Extend the fitted line to the extreme left of the plot. What would it predict as the cost for an office of size 5,000?

5. How well does the line fit the four observations with small capacity? For what size offices does the fitted line give reasonable estimates of cost?

135

Tree Age and Diameter (Curvature)

The table below lists 27 chestnut oak trees planted on a poor site with their ages and diameters at chest height. We would like to determine how their size increases with age.

Age in Years	Diameter at Chest Height in Inches
4	0.8
5	0.8
8	1.0
8	2.0
8	3.0
10	2.0
10	3.5
12	4.9
13	3.5
14	2.5
16	4.5
18	4.6
20	5.5
22	5.8
23	4.7
25	6.5
28	6.0
29	4.5
30	6.0
30	7.0
33	8.0
34	6.5
35	7.0
38	5.0
38	7.0
40	7.5
42	7.5

Source: Chapman and Demeritt, *Elements of Forest Mensuration.*

1. Make a scatter plot of these data. We want to predict diameter given age. Which variable will you put on the horizontal axis?

2. Divide the points into three strips. Mark the three X's and draw in the fitted line.

3. Do the three X's lie very close to a single straight line?

4. In the left strip, how many points are

    a. above the line?

    b. below the line?

5. In the center strip, how many points are

   a. above the line?

   b. below the line?

6. In the right strip, how many points are

   a. above the line?

   b. below the line?

There are too many points above the line in the center strip and too many points below the line in both end strips. This means that a single straight line does not fit these data well. A curved line would summarize these data better. There are more complicated statistical methods for fitting a curve to data, but we won't investigate them. You could draw a free-hand curve through the middle of the data.

7. The fact that the points lie on a curved line tells us that trees do not grow at the same rate over their lifetime. Does the diameter increase at a faster rate when the tree is young or old?

Lines on Scatter Plots — Summary

The scatter plot is the basic method for learning about relationships between two variables. Sometimes interpretations are clear simply from studying the scatter plot. This section has dealt with problems where the interpretation becomes clearer by adding a straight line to the plot.

The method of adding the $45°$ line ($y = x$ line) through the points $(0, 0)$, $(1, 1)$, $(2, 2)$, and so forth and then observing on which side of this line most points lie can assist us in learning whether the variable on the horizontal axis or the variable on the vertical axis is generally larger. This method does not require fitting a line to the data.

In some examples it is helpful to fit a straight line through the central part of the data. We have used a method based on medians. This method is not greatly affected by a few outlying points. If the data follow a straight-line relationship, the method described gives a line that fits the data closely. Moreover, looking at the data in terms of the three X's and the straight line can help us to recognize examples where the data do not fit a single straight line. These situations, such as clustering and curvature, need to be dealt with differently.

The critical feature about the $45°$ line and the fitted straight line is not just the method of constructing them. As with all the other methods in this book, their purpose is to assist you in the interpretation and analysis of the data. These straight lines can help identify interesting and important data points, find and summarize relationships between the variables, and predict the variable on the vertical axis from the variable on the horizontal axis.

Student Project

1. Take the scatter plots you made on your projects from Section VI and add straight lines when appropriate. Do the lines change any of your interpretations?

VIII. SMOOTHING PLOTS OVER TIME

The following table lists the American League home run champions from 1921 to 1985.

Year	American League	HR	Year	American League	HR
1921	Babe Ruth, New York	59	1957	Roy Sievers, Washington	42
1922	Ken Williams, St. Louis	39	1958	Mickey Mantle, New York	42
1923	Babe Ruth, New York	41	1959	Rocky Colavito, Cleveland	42
1924	Babe Ruth, New York	46		Harmon Killebrew, Washington	
1925	Bob Meusel, New York	33	1960	Mickey Mantle, New York	40
1926	Babe Ruth, New York	47	1961	Roger Maris, New York	61
1927	Babe Ruth, New York	60	1962	Harmon Killebrew, Minnesota	48
1928	Babe Ruth, New York	54	1963	Harmon Killebrew, Minnesota	45
1929	Babe Ruth, New York	46	1964	Harmon Killebrew, Minnesota	49
1930	Babe Ruth, New York	49	1965	Tony Conigliaro, Boston	32
1931	Babe Ruth, New York	46	1966	Frank Robinson, Baltimore	49
	Lou Gehrig, New York		1967	Carl Yastrzemski, Boston	44
1932	Jimmy Foxx, Philadelphia	58		Harmon Killebrew, Minnesota	
1933	Jimmy Foxx, Philadelphia	48	1968	Frank Howard, Washington	44
1934	Lou Gehrig, New York	49	1969	Harmon Killebrew, Minnesota	49
1935	Jimmy Foxx, Philadelphia	36	1970	Frank Howard, Washington	44
	Hank Greenberg, Detroit		1971	Bill Melton, Chicago	33
1936	Lou Gehrig, New York	49	1972	Dick Allen, Chicago	37
1937	Joe DiMaggio, New York	46	1973	Reggie Jackson, Oakland	32
1938	Hank Greenberg, Detroit	58	1974	Dick Allen, Chicago	32
1939	Jimmy Foxx, Boston	35	1975	George Scott, Milwaukee	36
1940	Hank Greenberg, Detroit	41		Reggie Jackson, Oakland	
1941	Ted Williams, Boston	37	1976	Graig Nettles, New York	32
1942	Ted Williams, Boston	36	1977	Jim Rice, Boston	39
1943	Rudy York, Detroit	34	1978	Jim Rice, Boston	46
1944	Nick Etten, New York	22	1979	Gorman Thomas, Milwaukee	45
1945	Vern Stephens, St. Louis	24	1980	Reggie Jackson, New York	41
1946	Hank Greenberg, Detroit	44		Ben Oglivie, Milwaukee	
1947	Ted Williams, Boston	32	1981	Bobby Grich, California	22
1948	Joe DiMaggio, New York	39		Tony Armas, Oakland	
1949	Ted Williams, Boston	43		Dwight Evans, Boston	
1950	Al Rosen, Cleveland	37		Eddie Murray, Baltimore	
1951	Gus Zernial, Chicago-Philadelphia	33	1982	Gorman Thomas, Milwaukee	39
1952	Larry Doby, Cleveland	32		Reggie Jackson, California	
1953	Al Rosen, Cleveland	43	1983	Jim Rice, Boston	39
1954	Larry Doby, Cleveland	32	1984	Tony Armas, Boston	43
1955	Mickey Mantle, New York	37	1985	Darrell Evans, Detroit	40
1956	Mickey Mantle, New York	52			

Source: *The World Almanac and Book of Facts,* 1985 edition.

From this list it is difficult to see any general trends in the number of home runs through the years. To try to determine the general trends, we will make a scatter plot over time of the number of home runs hit by the champions and connect these points.

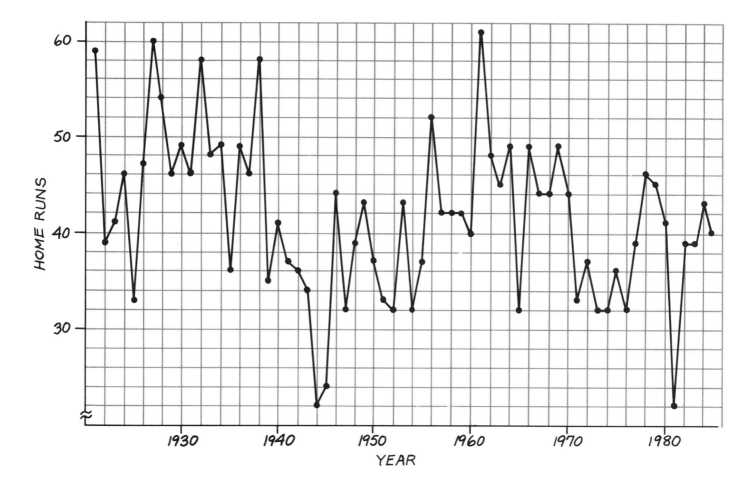

This scatter plot looks all jumbled up! It is impossible to see general trends because of the large fluctuations in the number of home runs hit from year to year. For example, 58 home runs were hit in 1938 compared to only 35 the next year. This variation gives the plot a sawtooth effect. The highs and lows, not the overall pattern, capture our attention. To remove the large fluctuations from the data, we will use a method called *smoothing*.

To illustrate, the smoothed version of the first ten years of the home run champions' data follows.

Year	Home Runs	Smoothed Values
1921	59	59
1922	39	41
1923	41	41
1924	46	41
1925	33	46
1926	47	47
1927	60	54
1928	54	54
1929	46	49
1930	49	46
1931	46	

139

To find the smoothed value for 1924, for example, the 46 home runs for that year are compared to the number of home runs for the year before, 41, and the number of home runs for the following year, 33. The median of the three numbers, 41, is entered into the smoothed values column.

For the first and last years, just copy the original data into the smoothed values column.

The plot of the connected smoothed values follows. Notice what has happened to the large fluctuation between 1938 and 1939. Since this plot is smoother than the previous one, we can see general trends better, such as the drop in the number of home runs in the 1940's.

Discussion Questions

1. Complete the smoothed value column through 1940 for the next ten American League home run champions.

2. Study the smoothed plot of the American League home run champions.

   a. What happened around 1940 that could have affected the number of home runs hit?

   b. Did the increase in the number of games from 154 to 162 in 1961 have an effect on the number of home runs hit?

3. Study the following rule changes. Do any of them seem to have affected the number of home runs hit by the champions?

   1926 — A ball hit over a fence that is less than 250 feet from home plate will not be counted as a home run.

   1931 — A fair ball that bounces over a fence will be counted as a double instead of a home run.

   1959 — New ballparks must have a minimum distance of 325 feet down the foul lines and 400 feet in center field.

   1969 — The strike zone is decreased in size to include only the area from the armpit to the top of the knee.

   1969 — The pitcher's mound is lowered, giving an advantage to the hitter.

   1971 — All batters must wear helmets.

4. In 1981 there was a strike that shortened the season. Can this be seen in the original data? In the smoothed values?

5. Since they were not smoothed, the endpoints may appear to be out of place. The number of home runs hit in 1921 seems too high. Can you determine a better rule for deciding what to write in the smoothed values column for the endpoints?

6. Imagine a curve through the smoothed values. Try to predict the number of home runs hit in 1986.

7. Some students feel that smoothing is not a legitimate method. For example, they do not like changing the original 33 home runs in 1925 to 46 home runs on the plot of smoothed values. Write a description of the trends that are visible in the smoothed plot that are not easily seen in the original plot. Try to convince a reluctant fellow student that smoothing is valuable. Then study the following answer. Did you mention features we omitted?

The original plot of the time series for home runs gives a very jagged appearance. There were values that were quite large for two years in the 1920's, two years in the 1930's, and also in 1961. Extremely low values occurred in the mid-1940's and in 1981. Using this plot, it is difficult to evaluate overall trends. However, the values in the 1940's and early 1950's seem lower than the values in the late 1920's and 1930's.

We get a stronger impression of trends from the smoothed plot of the home run data. In particular, for the years from 1927 to 1935, the values are generally higher than at any other time before or since. The only period that was nearly comparable was in the early 1960's. The original data show that the champions causing the earlier values to be large were Babe Ruth, Jimmy Foxx, and Lou Gehrig. In the 1960's, it was Roger Maris and Harmon Killebrew. These players clearly were outstanding home run hitters!

There was a steady decline in home runs from the late 1930's to a low period in the middle 1940's. There were also low periods in the early 1950's and in the early 1970's. It is interesting that these lows coincide roughly with World War II, the Korean War, and the Viet Nam War. These wars might be possible causes for the declines, although we have not proved this simply through observing this association. The values for the years since 1980 are near the middle compared to the whole 65-year series. The smoothed series has removed some of the individual highs (such as Maris' 61 in 1961) and lows (such as the 22 in the strike-shortened 1981 season). Therefore, the longer trends stand out more clearly.

Birth Months

The following table gives the number of babies born in the United States for each month of 1984. The numbers are in thousands.

Month	Births (thousands)	Smoothed Values
January	314	
February	289	
March	291	
April	302	
May	296	
June	297	
July	336	
August	323	
September	329	
October	316	
November	292	
December	311	

Source: National Center for Health Statistics.

1. How many babies were born in May 1984?

2. In which month were the most babies born?

The time series plot for these data is given as follows. This plot is a good candidate for smoothing because of the sawtooth effect. This appearance is an indication that some points are unusually large or small.

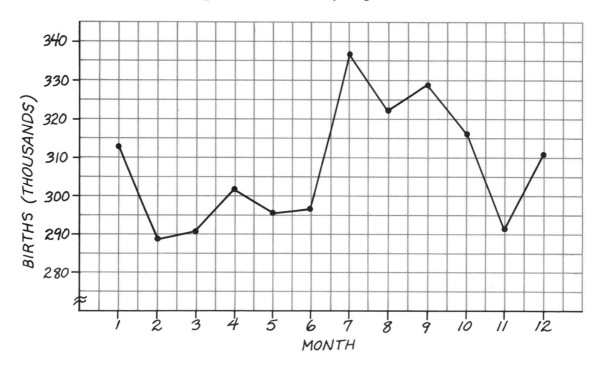

3. Copy and complete the "Smoothed Values" column.

4. Make a scatter plot of the smoothed values.

5. What is the general trend in the number of babies born throughout the year?

Application 36

Olympic Marathon

The following table shows the winning times for the marathon run (slightly more than 26 miles) in the 1896-1984 Olympics. The times are rounded to the nearest minute.

Year	Winner Name, Country	Time			Time in Minutes	Smoothed Values
1896	Loues, Greece	2 hours	59 minutes		179	
1900	Teato, France	3	0		180	
1904	Hicks, U.S.A.	3	29		209	
1908	Hayes, U.S.A.	2	55		175	
1912	McArthur, South Africa	2	37		157	
1920	Kolehmainen, Finland	2	33		153	
1924	Stenroos, Finland	2	41		161	
1928	El Ouafi, France	2	33		153	
1932	Zabala, Argentina	2	32		152	
1936	Son, Japan	2	29		149	
1948	Cabrera, Argentina	2	35			
1952	Zatopek, Czechoslovakia	2	23			
1956	Mimoun, France	2	25			
1960	Bikila, Ethiopia	2	15			
1964	Bikila, Ethiopia	2	12			
1968	Wolde, Ethiopia	2	20			
1972	Shorter, U.S.A.	2	12			
1976	Cierpinski, East Germany	2	10			
1980	Cierpinski, East Germany	2	11			
1984	Lopes, Portugal	2	9			

Source: *The World Almanac and Book of Facts,* 1985 edition.

1. The first Olympic women's marathon was not held until 1984. The winner was Joan Benoit of the United States with a time of 2 hours 25 minutes. What was the first year that a Olympic men's marathon winner was able to beat this time?

2. Find the three years when the Olympics were not held. Why were the Olympics not held in these years?

3. Complete the second to the last column of the previous table by converting each time to minutes. The first ten are done for you.

A plot over time with year on the horizontal axis and time in minutes on the vertical axis is shown as follows:

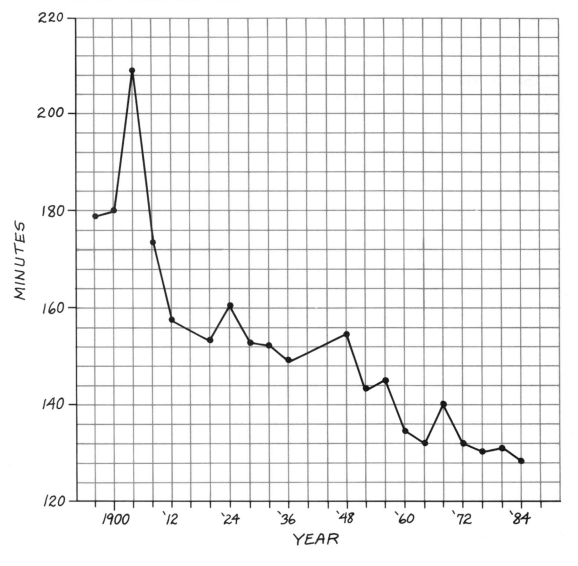

4. What trends do you see in this plot?

5. On the time series plot, which year is farthest from the general trend?

6. Complete the last column of the previous table by smoothing the "time in minutes" column.

7. Construct a plot over time for the smoothed values.

8. Study your plot over time for the smoothed values.

    a. When did the largest drop in time occur?

    b. What do you predict for the winning time in the 1988 Olympic marathon?

    c. Describe the patterns shown on your plot in a short paragraph.

Application 37

Tennis Earnings

The following two tables from *Tennis Championships Magazine* list the top tennis players of each sex and their earnings from tennis tournaments in the first part of 1985.

The Top 32 Women

Name	Birthplace	Height	Weight	Age	Computer Ranking	1985 Earnings
Chris Evert Lloyd	Ft. Lauderdale, FL	5'6"	118	30	1	$652,269
Martina Navratilova	Czechoslovakia	5'7"	145	28	2	994,579
Hana Mandlikova	Czechoslovakia	5'8"	130	23	3	294,872
Pam Shriver	Baltimore, MD	5'11"	130	23	4	244,653
Manuela Maleeva	Bulgaria	5'6"	114	18	5	115,113
Helena Sukova	Czechoslovakia	6'1"	139	20	6	261,512
Zina Garrison	Houston, TX	5'4"	128	21	7	162,732
Claudia Kohde-Kilsch	West Germany	6'0"	140	21	8	181,995
Wendy Turnbull	Australia	5'4"	120	32	9	104,795
Kathy Rinaldi	Stuart, FL	5'5"	110	18	10	120,315
Bonnie Gadusek	Pittsburgh, PA	5'6"	120	21	11	88,097
Steffi Graf	West Germany	5'5"	110	16	12	81,872
Catarina Lindqvist	Sweden	5'5"	125	22	13	107,805
Gabriela Sabatini	Argentina	5'7"	121	15	14	85,405
Carling Bassett	Canada	5'5"	118	17	15	113,173
Barbara Potter	Waterbury, CT	5'9"	135	23	16	82,949
Kathy Jordan	Bryn Mawr, PA	5'8"	130	25	17	149,763
Bettina Bunge	Switzerland	5'7"	120	22	18	72,090
Sylvia Hanika	West Germany	5'8"	128	25	19	32,310
Andrea Temesvari	Hungary	5'11"	125	19	20	49,810
Alycia Moulton	Sacramento, CA	5'11"	145	24	21	58,735
Peanut Louie	San Francisco, CA	5'5"	115	25	22	48,850
Pam Casale	Camden, NJ	5'8"	127	21	23	43,965
Gigi Fernandez	Puerto Rico	5'7"	140	21	24	56,850
Kathleen Horvath	Chicago, IL	5'7"	115	20	25	68,962
Michelle Torres	Chicago, IL	5'5"	107	18	26	10,950
Elise Burgin	Baltimore, MD	5'4"	115	23	27	68,806
Katerina Maleeva	Bulgaria	5'5"	110	16	28	54,897
Rosalyn Fairbank	South Africa	5'8"	140	24	29	81,301
Catherine Tanvier	France	5'8"	116	20	30	45,660
Virginia Ruzici	Romania	5'8"	128	30	31	49,757
Pascale Paradis	France	5'9"	135	19	32	42,017

Source: *Tennis Championships Magazine.*

The Top 32 Men

Name	Birthplace	Height	Weight	Age	Computer Ranking	1985 Earnings
John McEnroe	West Germany	5'11"	165	26	1	$618,852
Ivan Lendl	Czechoslovakia	6'2"	175	25	2	609,283
Mats Wilander	Sweden	6'1"	175	21	3	416,037
Jimmy Connors	Belleville, IL	5'10"	155	32	4	375,291
Kevin Curren	South Africa	6'1"	170	27	5	193,422
Anders Jarryd	Sweden	5'11"	155	24	6	248,133
Yannick Noah	France	6'4"	180	25	7	202,899
Andres Gomez	Ecuador	6'3"	190	25	8	99,794
Boris Becker	West Germany	6'2"	173	17	9	278,207
Joakim Nystrom	Sweden	6'2"	155	22	10	192,583
Stefan Edberg	Sweden	6'2"	158	19	11	169,920
Eliot Teltscher	Palos Verdes, CA	5'10"	150	26	12	81,092
Miloslav Mecir	Czechoslovakia	6'3"	180	21	13	209,172
Johan Kriek	South Africa	5'8"	155	27	14	151,991
Pat Cash	Australia	5'11"	170	20	15	123,244
Tim Mayotte	Springfield, MA	6'3"	180	25	16	255,174
Scott Davis	Santa Monica, CA	6'2"	170	22	17	126,324
Henrik Sundstrom	Sweden	6'2"	160	21	18	140,122
Tomas Smid	Czechoslovakia	6'3"	175	29	19	220,043
Brad Gilbert	Oakland, CA	6'1"	160	24	20	92,667
Martin Jaite	Argentina	5'11"	150	20	21	104,985
David Pate	Los Angeles, CA	6'0"	170	23	22	84,798
Aaron Krickstein	Ann Arbor, MI	5'10"	150	18	23	110,965
Greg Holmes	Covina, CA	5'10"	160	21	24	56,092
Vitas Gerulaitis	Brooklyn, NY	6'0"	155	31	25	54,329
Libor Pimek	Czechoslovakia	6'5"	172	22	26	61,542
Henri Leconte	France	6'1"	160	22	27	101,690
Jose Luis Clerc	Argentina	6'1"	176	27	28	46,356
Jan Gunnarsson	Sweden	6'0"	165	23	29	81,694
Ben Testerman	Knoxville, TN	6'3"	180	23	30	40,557
Sammy Giammalva	Houston, TX	5'10"	165	22	31	78,873
Jimmy Arias	Buffalo, NY	5'9"	145	21	32	79,941

Source: *Tennis Championships Magazine.*

Do this activity in pairs, with one of you taking the data for men and the other the data for women. After you each answer questions separately for your players, you will put your plots together to compare the women's earnings with the men's. You will need to coordinate with your partner so you both use the same size graph paper.

1. Construct a plot over time of the earnings against the computer ranking for your players. Begin by plotting the 32 values as dots; do not connect them with lines. Because the first few men and women earned so much more than the rest, a vertical axis that includes all the earnings would result in most of the earnings being too close together at the bottom. Instead, make the vertical axis from $0 to $400,000. For those

players who earned more than this, just write in their numbers at the top.

2. In the earlier examples, to get the smoothed earnings we constructed a column of smoothed values and then plotted them. This time we will save a step and do this directly on the plot. For each rank, plot an X at the median of the three earnings from that rank, the next lower rank, and the next higher rank. (You might also want to use a different color from the dots for the X's to help distinguish the actual earnings from the smoothed earnings.)

3. Connect the X's by lines. This gives a smooth curve relating the 1985 earnings to the computer rankings.

4. Name any players that have earned a relatively large amount, or a relatively small amount, considering their ranking. Can you think of any reasons for this to happen?

5. The earnings generally decrease as the computer ranking increases. Do the earnings decrease more quickly for the very top ranked players or for the lower ranked players?

6. Give an estimate of how much money you would expect the player who is fifth ranked in 1986 to earn in the corresponding part of 1986.

To answer the remaining questions, work with your partner so you have plots for both men and women.

7. Is smoothing more helpful for the men's data or the women's data to get a useful picture of how earnings relate to rank?

8. Which top tennis players earn more, men or women? To compare the earnings, it helps to place the two plots on top of each other and hold them up to a light. Write a paragraph summarizing how the women's and men's earnings compare.

Advanced Smoothing (Optional)

Often the smoothing method we have just used will give a smooth curve. Sometimes, however, it will still have fluctuations in it that can hide overall trends. In these cases, we will want to smooth the data a little bit more.

For example, in the plot of smoothed values for the American League home run leaders on page 140, the points for the years 1927, 1928, 1944, and 1945 are separated from the general trend. They still give that sawtooth appearance that obscures the overall pattern. A simple method for further smoothing is described in the following paragraphs.

One result of what we did to the first ten years of American League home run data was to make some short strings where adjacent values are equal. For example, the smoothed values for 1922 to 1924 are all 41. One possibility is to treat such "horizontal ties" as single points, and then do the smoothing a second time.

To illustrate, the data for the first ten years, the first smoothed values, and the second smoothed values are listed in the following table.

Year	Home Runs	First Smoothed Values	Second Smoothed Values
1921	59	59	59
1922	39	41	46
1923	41	41	46
1924	46	41	46
1925	33	46	46
1926	47	47	47
1927	60	54	49
1928	54	54	49
1929	46	49	49
1930	49	46	

To find the second smoothed values, we use only the first smoothed values. For the first year, 1921, the value is simply retained. For 1922, we treat the three adjacent 41's as a single value and find the median of 59, 41, and 46, which is 46. For 1923 and 1924, we have the median of 59, 41, and 46 again. For 1925, use the median of 41, 46, and 47. For 1926, use the median of 46, 47, and 54. Use the median of 47, 54, and 49 for 1927 and 1928. For 1929, use the median of 54, 49, and 46.

The plot of the second smoothed values follows. Notice that these smoothed values show the overall trends somewhat more clearly than the earlier smoothed values. Almost all the points that lie far away from the others have been smoothed away. It is now easy to imagine a smooth curve that connects most of the points.

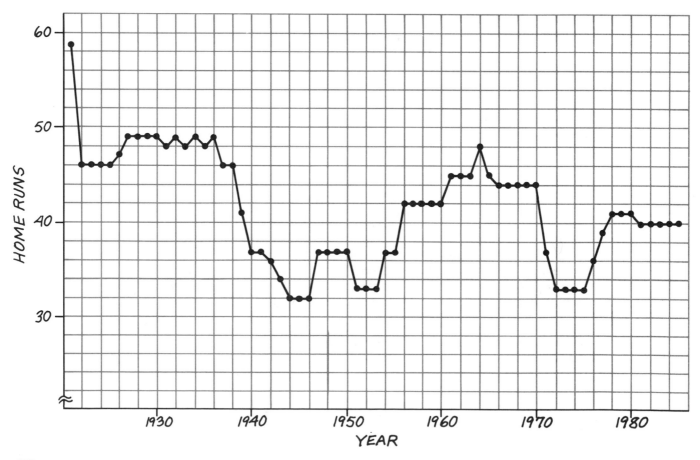

Discussion Questions

1. Complete the next ten values in the second column of smoothed values for the American League home run champions.

2. Which period had the most home runs? Who was responsible for this occurrence?

3. When were the periods of fewest home runs? What was happening during these years?

4. Compare the original home run champions' data to the smoother curve just shown. Which champions differed the most from the value of the overall trend when they played?

This same smoothing process can be repeated to get third smoothed values that are even smoother than the second ones. Using the second smoothed values and the same exact method that was used to calculate the second smoothed values from the first smoothed values, you can calculate the third smoothed values. The effect will be to remove even more of the "bumpiness." For these particular data, the third smoothed values will remove the small peak in 1947-1950 and lower the peak in 1964.

National League Home Run Champions (Optional)

The following table lists the National League home run champions.

Year	National League	HR	First Smoothed Values
1921	George Kelly, New York	23	23
1922	Rogers Hornsby, St. Louis	42	41
1923	Cy Williams, Philadelphia	41	41
1924	Jacques Foumier, Brooklyn	27	39
1925	Rogers Hornsby, St. Louis	39	27
1926	Hack Wilson, Chicago	21	30
1927	Hack Wilson, Chicago Cy Williams, Philadelphia	30	30
1928	Hack Wilson, Chicago Jim Bottomley, St. Louis	31	31
1929	Charles Klein, Philadelphia	43	43
1930	Hack Wilson, Chicago	56	43
1931	Charles Klein, Philadelphia	31	38
1932	Charles Klein, Philadelphia Mel Ott, New York	38	31
1933	Charles Klein, Philadelphia	28	35
1934	Rip Collins, St. Louis Mel Ott, New York	35	34
1935	Walter Berger, Boston	34	34
1936	Mel Ott, New York	33	33
1937	Mel Ott, New York Joe Medwick, St. Louis	31	33
1938	Mel Ott, New York	36	31
1939	John Mize, St. Louis	28	36
1940	John Mize, St. Louis	43	34
1941	Dolph Camilli, Brooklyn	34	34
1942	Mel Ott, New York	30	30
1943	Bill Nicholson, Chicago	29	30
1944	Bill Nicholson, Chicago	33	29
1945	Tommy Holmes, Boston	28	28
1946	Ralph Kiner, Pittsburgh	23	28
1947	Ralph Kiner, Pittsburgh John Mize, New York	51	40
1948	Ralph Kiner, Pittsburgh John Mize, New York	40	51
1949	Ralph Kiner, Pittsburgh	54	47
1950	Ralph Kiner, Pittsburgh	47	47
1951	Ralph Kiner, Pittsburgh	42	42

Source: *The World Almanac and Book of Facts,* 1985 edition.

Year	National League	HR	First Smoothed Values
1952	Ralph Kiner, Pittsburgh	37	42
	Hank Sauer, Chicago		
1953	Ed Mathews, Milwaukee	47	47
1954	Ted Kluszewski, Cincinnati	49	49
1955	Willie Mays, New York	51	49
1956	Duke Snider, Brooklyn	43	44
1957	Hank Aaron, Milwaukee	44	44
1958	Ernie Banks, Chicago	47	46
1959	Ed Mathews, Milwaukee	46	46
1960	Ernie Banks, Chicago	41	46
1961	Orlando Cepeda, San Francisco	46	46
1962	Willie Mays, San Francisco	49	46
1963	Hank Aaron, Milwaukee	44	47
	Willie McCovey, San Francisco		
1964	Willie Mays, San Francisco	47	47
1965	Willie Mays, San Francisco	52	47
1966	Hank Aaron, Atlanta	44	44
1967	Hank Aaron, Atlanta	39	39
1968	Willie McCovey, San Francisco	36	39
1969	Willie McCovey, San Francisco	45	45
1970	Johnny Bench, Cincinnati	45	45
1971	Willie Stargell, Pittsburgh	48	45
1972	Johnny Bench, Cincinnati	40	44
1973	Willie Stargell, Pittsburgh	44	40
1974	Mike Schmidt, Philadelphia	36	38
1975	Mike Schmidt, Philadelphia	38	38
1976	Mike Schmidt, Philadelphia	38	38
1977	George Foster, Cincinnati	52	40
1978	George Foster, Cincinnati	40	48
1979	Dave Kingman, Chicago	48	48
1980	Mike Schmidt, Philadelphia	48	48
1981	Mike Schmidt, Philadelphia	31	37
1982	Dave Kingman, New York	37	37
1983	Mike Schmidt, Philadelphia	40	37
1984	Mike Schmidt, Philadelphia	36	37
	Dale Murphy, Atlanta		
1985	Dale Murphy, Atlanta	37	37

Source: *The World Almanac and Book of Facts,* 1985 edition.

1. Which player hit the largest number of home runs in a season?
2. Which player was champion for the most seasons?

A plot over time of the number of home runs follows:

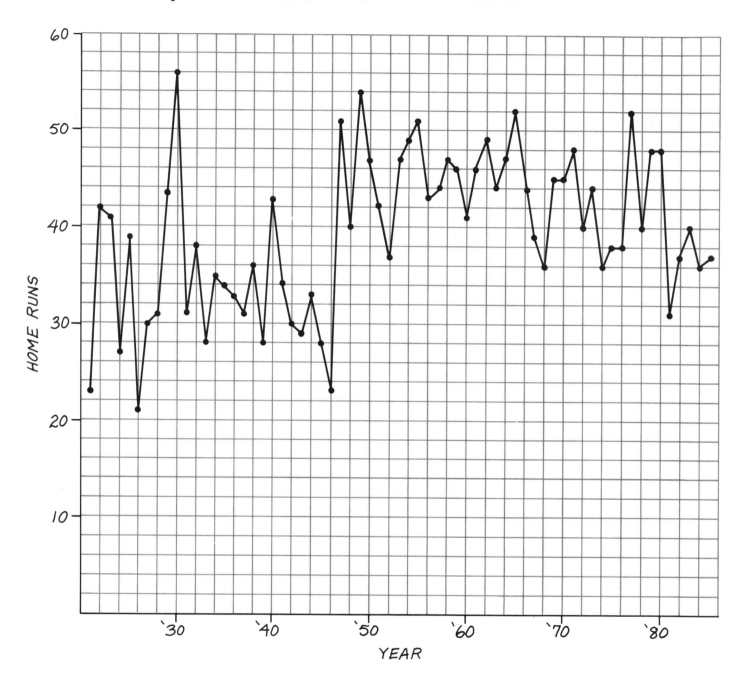

3. From this plot, it is easy to spot unusually high or low years. Which years stand out as the most unusual?

A plot over time of the smoothed values follows:

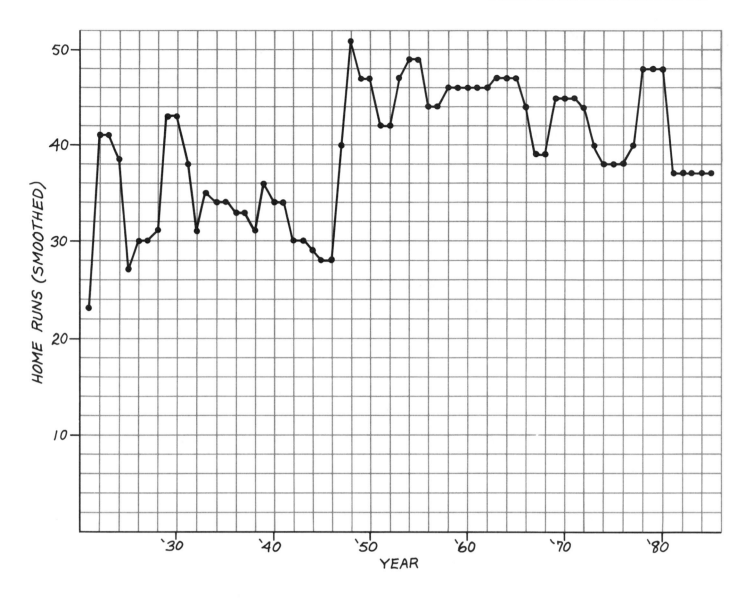

4. Is there a dip in the early 1940's (during World War II) as there was for the American League?

5. Are there any other especially noticeable trends in this plot?

6. This is an example where a second smoothing might be useful for spotting overall trends. Using the method described just before this application, use the column of first smoothed values and add a column of second smoothed values.

7. Construct a plot over time using the second smoothed values.

8. What has been happening to the number of home runs since 1950?

9. How did the numbers of home runs in the 1920's and 1930's compare to the numbers in the 1960's and 1970's?

10. Do you think that the second smoothed value for 1921 is reasonable? Try to invent a method to smooth endpoints.

11. When did the largest increase in home runs occur?

12. What do you think was the winning number of home runs in 1986?

13. For which year is the actual data value the farthest above the second smoothed value? For which year is the data value the farthest below the second smoothed value?

14. Compare the second smoothed curve for the American League home runs with the second smoothed curve for the National League. What is one way that these curves are similar? What is one way that they are different?

15. Since 1960, are the trends in both leagues about the same?

Smoothing Plots Over Time — Summary

Smoothing is a technique that can be used with time series data where the horizontal axis is marked off in years, days, hours, ages, and so forth. We can use medians to obtain smoothed values, and these smoothed values can remove much of the sawtooth effect often seen in time series data. As a result, a clearer picture of where values are increasing and decreasing emerges.

Many students feel uncomfortable with smoothing. Try to think of it in the same way you think about computing, say, a mean. When you average your test scores in math, the original scores disappear and you are left with one number that summarizes how well you did overall. It is a similar idea with smoothing. Some of the original data disappear and you are left with a summary of overall trends.

Suggestions for Student Projects

1. If any of the scatter plots from your projects in Section VI were plots over time, smooth those plots. Does this show any of the trends more clearly than before?

2. Collect some time series data that interest you and analyze these data according to the methods of this section. Your topic might be one of the following:

   • the number of student absences in your class or school for each day of the last few months

   • daily sales in the school cafeteria during the last few months

   • the daily temperature maximums, minimums, or ranges as reported in the local newspaper

   • sports records for your school

3. A variation of the procedure for smoothing is to replace each value with the median of that value and the *two* values on either side. For example, in the American League home run data, the smoothed value for 1924 would be 41, which is the median of 39, 41, 46, 33, and 47. These are the number of home runs hit in 1922, 1923, 1924, 1925, and 1926. Use this method of "smoothing by medians of five values" on the American League home run data. Discuss the advantages and disadvantages over the usual method.

IX. REVIEW OF ALL TECHNIQUES

It might be helpful to reread the review of one variable techniques in Section V before reading this section.

Two Variable Techniques

Suppose that we have measured the cumulative grade point average and the SAT score for each senior in a school. We want to learn how grade point averages and SAT scores are related. This is called a *two variable* situation since we have two values, grade average and test score, for each person.

The basic display for this situation is the scatter plot (Section VI). From a scatter plot you can determine if there is positive, negative, or no association between the variables. You can also determine whether or not the data separate into several clusters of points and whether or not there are any outlying points that do not follow the general pattern. If you notice one of these features, try to find possible reasons for it as part of your interpretation. Often in scatter plots, one of the two variables is time. In these situations we have a plot over time (Section VI).

After constructing and studying a scatter plot, the relationship between the variables may be clear. If so, there is no need to supplement the scatter plot. However, important yet subtle interpretations, concerning both general relationships and specific data points, can often be brought out by adding an appropriate straight line to the scatter plot (Section VII). For plots over time, smoothing can help to show long-run underlying trends, as well as departures of specific points from these trends (Section VIII).

The following applications will help you to see the relative advantages and disadvantages of the statistical methods described in Sections I-VIII. No new techniques are given. These applications will take more time and thought than previous ones as you will have to decide which plot is the best.

There are no right or wrong answers to many of the questions. Your teacher will expect you to make plots that are appropriate and to write thoughtful and complete comments about the characteristics of the data shown in the plot.

Presidential Autographs

The following table lists the U.S. presidents. With each is the lowest price you could expect to pay for his autograph (a plain signature).

Washington, George	$450	Arthur, Chester A.	$30
Adams, John	300	Cleveland, Grover	26
Jefferson, Thomas	400	Harrison, Benjamin	28
Madison, James	100	McKinley, William	38
Monroe, James	75	Roosevelt, Theodore	32
Adams, John Q.	80	Taft, William H.	28
Jackson, Andrew	150	Wilson, Woodrow	38
Van Buren, Martin	65	Harding, Warren G.	28
Harrison, William H.	80	Coolidge, Calvin	28
Tyler, John	60	Hoover, Herbert	28
Polk, James K.	60	Roosevelt, Franklin	33
Taylor, Zachary	60	Truman, Harry	39
Fillmore, Millard	50	Eisenhower, Dwight D.	28
Pierce, Franklin	50	Kennedy, John F.	80
Buchanan, James	50	Johnson, Lyndon B.	35
Lincoln, Abraham	350	Nixon, Richard M.	50
Johnson, Andrew	50	Ford, Gerald	28
Grant, U. S.	40	Carter, James E.	25
Hayes, Rutherford B.	30	Reagan, Ronald W.	25
Garfield, James	38		

Source: *The Official Price Guide to Paper Collectibles, 1985.*

1. Which president's autograph costs the most?

2. Which president's autograph costs the least?

3. Theodore Roosevelt became president in 1901, and all those preceding him in this list were president before 1900. We want to compare the prices of autographs for those who were president before 1900 with the prices for who were president since 1900. Use any two of the three types of plots — line, stem-and-leaf, or box — to make this comparison.

4. Which plot do you prefer? Why?

5. From this plot, estimate the median prices of autographs of presidents before 1900 and the median prices of autographs of presidents after 1900.

6. Do you think that presidents' autographs become more valuable as they get older? Construct the appropriate plot over time. If it seems to be helpful, make a plot of the smoothed values.

7. Write a summary of the information that you have learned about presidential autographs.

Least and Most Expensive Cities

The following table lists some major world cities. With each are the cost in dollars of one night for a single room in a good mid-range hotel and the cost of dinner for one including wine and a tip in a good restaurant.

CITY	HOTEL	DINNER
Athens	$23.73	$10.79
Caracas	24.82	10.95
New Delhi	34.18	12.70
Frankfurt	33.59	5.60
Hong Kong	45.86	19.11
Johannesburg	36.04	22.52
Lisbon	28.90	5.62
London	67.39	19.97
Madrid	30.81	6.56
Manila	81.80	27.27
Mexico City	46.82	13.38
Nairobi	22.22	5.93
New York	60.00	20.00
Paris	74.18	30.91
Rio de Janeiro	46.41	14.97
Rome	43.67	17.47
Stockholm	50.69	19.01
Sydney	54.11	17.75
Tokyo	48.24	16.35
Toronto	50.26	13.78
Vienna	39.77	10.60
Zurich	45.89	13.77

Source: Murray J. Brown, "Hotel and Dining Prices in Cities," *Los Angeles Times*, November 13, 1983.

1. Which city has the most expensive dinner? Which has the least expensive hotel?

To answer the following questions, you will have to decide which type of plot must be constructed and then construct it.

2. In which city is the cost of dinner relatively expensive compared to the cost of a hotel?

3. If the cost of a hotel room in a particular city is $50, what would you expect the cost of a dinner to be?

4. Write a description of the information displayed in your plot.

159

Who Was the Greatest Yankee Home Run Hitter?

The following table lists four of the greatest New York Yankees' home run hitters with the number of home runs each hit while a Yankee.

Babe Ruth		Lou Gehrig		Mickey Mantle		Roger Maris	
Year	Home Runs	Year	Home Runs	Year	Home Runs	Year	Home Runs
1920	54	1923	1	1951	13	1960	39
1921	59	1924	0	1952	23	1961	61
1922	35	1925	20	1953	21	1962	33
1923	41	1926	16	1954	27	1963	23
1924	46	1927	47	1955	37	1964	26
1925	25	1928	27	1956	52	1965	8
1926	47	1929	35	1957	34	1966	13
1927	60	1930	41	1958	42		
1928	54	1931	46	1959	31		
1929	46	1932	34	1960	40		
1930	49	1933	32	1961	54		
1931	46	1934	49	1962	30		
1932	41	1935	30	1963	15		
1933	34	1936	49	1964	35		
1934	22	1937	37	1965	19		
		1938	29	1966	23		
		1939	0	1967	22		
				1968	18		

Source: *Macmillan Baseball Encyclopedia*, 4th edition.

1. Study these records. Which player appears to be the greatest home run hitter? Why did you choose this player?

2. Your task now is to rank the four players. You may wish to compute means, medians, or quartiles, or make line plots, stem-and-leaf plots, box plots, plots over time, or smoothed plots over time.

   How did you rank the four players? Describe your reasons and include your plots.

Application 42

Yankees Versus Mets

New York City has two baseball teams, the Yankees and the Mets. The following table gives the attendance and final standing for both teams each year since the Mets began play in 1962. There are no questions for this application. Your assignment is to make the plots you think are appropriate and interesting. Then write a report about your discoveries.

Here is a possible question to get you started: In a year when attendance for the Yankees is high does Mets attendance also tend to be high?

	YANKEES			METS	
Finish	Attendance	Year	Attendance	Finish
Second	2,214,587	1985	2,751,437	Second
Third	1,821,815	1984	1,829,482	Second
Third	2,257,976	1983	1,103,808	Sixth
Fifth	2,041,219	1982	1,320,055	Sixth
First	1,614,533	1981	701,910	Fifth
First	2,627,417	1980	1,178,659	Fifth
Fourth	2,537,765	1979	788,905	Sixth
First	2,335,871	1978	1,007,328	Sixth
First	2,103,092	1977	1,066,825	Sixth
First	2,012,434	1976	1,468,754	Third
Third	1,288,048	1975	1,730,566	Third
Second	1,273,075	1974	1,722,209	Fifth
Fourth	1,262,077	1973	1,912,390	First
Fourth	966,328	1972	2,134,185	Third
Fourth	1,070,771	1971	2,266,680	Third
Second	1,136,879	1970	2,697,479	Third
Fifth	1,067,996	1969	2,175,373	First
Fifth	1,125,124	1968	1,781,657	Ninth
Ninth	1,141,714	1967	1,565,492	Tenth
Tenth	1,124,648	1966	1,932,693	Ninth
Sixth	1,213,552	1965	1,768,389	Tenth
First	1,305,636	1964	1,732,597	Tenth
First	1,308,920	1963	1,080,108	Tenth
First	1,493,574	1962	922,530	Tenth

Source: *Newark Star-Ledger,* April 7, 1985.

161

ACKNOWLEDGMENTS

Grateful acknowledgment is made to the following publishers, authors, and institutions for permission to use and adapt copyrighted materials.

Addison-Wesley Publishing Company for data on page 111 on World War II submarine sinkings, from Mosteller, Fienberg, and Rourke, *Beginning Statistics with Data Analysis*, © 1983, Addison-Wesley, Reading, Massachusetts. Pg. 79, Table 3-3. Reprinted with permission.

American Public Health Association for data on page 119 on coronary heart disease, from "Cigarette Smoking Related to Geographic Variations in Coronary Heart Disease Mortality and to Expectation of Life in the Two Sexes," Risteard Mulcahy, J.W. McGiluary, and Noel Hickey, in *American Journal of Public Health*, vol. 60, 1970.

Ballantine Books for data on page 158 on the value of presidential autographs, from *The Official Price Guide to Paper Collectibles*, edited by Thomas E. Hudgeons, © 1985, Ballantine Books, New York, NY 10022.

Beverage World for data on page 18 on U.S. soft drink consumption. Reprinted by permission from *Beverage World*, March 1978.

R. R. Bowker Company for data on page 32 on sales of children's books, from *Eighty Years of Best Sellers*, A. P. Hackett and J. H. Burke. Copyright © 1977, R. R. Bowker Company, New York, NY 10017.

Murray J. Brown for data on page 159 on least and most expensive cities, from "Hotel and Dining Prices in Cities" in the *Los Angeles Times*, November 13, 1983. Reprinted by permission of the author.

Peter H. Brown for the "Dumbing for Dollars" chart on page 90, adapted from an article in the *Los Angeles Times*, January 20, 1985. Reprinted by permission of the author.

Consumers Union for data on page 7 from "Nutritional Information for Fast Foods" in *Consumer Reports*; for data and excerpts on pages 36–37 from "How Does Your Allowance Compare to Others," and for data on page 45 from "Motocross Bike Ratings," both in *Penny Power*; also, for data on page 95 from "Walkaround Stereos" in the *1985 Buying Guide Issue*. Copyright 1979, 1983, 1985 by Consumers Union of the United States, Inc., Mount Vernon, NY 10553. Reprinted by permission from *Consumer Reports*, September 1979, *Penny Power*, February/March 1983, and the *1985 Buying Guide Issue*.

Consumers Union of the United States, Inc., Mount Vernon, NY 10553. Reprinted by permission from *Consumer Reports*, September 1979, *Penny Power*, February/March 1983, and the *1985 Buying Guide Issue*.

Highway Loss Data Institute for data on page 65 on automobile safety records. Copyright Highway Loss Data Institute, Washington, DC 20037.

Joint Center for Political Studies for data on page 108 on the number of black state legislators. Reprinted by permission.

P. J. Kenedy & Sons for data on page 121 on the Catholic clergy, from *The Official Catholic Directory 1985*, published by P. J. Kenedy & Sons, New York, NY 10022.

Los Angeles Times for data on page 3 on top 10 record albums, from "The King of Hearts vs. the Queen of Tarts," Robert Hilburn, copyright 1985, *Los Angeles Times*. Reprinted by permission. For data on page 41 on record album ratings, from "The Pop Meter," copyright 1985, *Los Angeles Times*. Reprinted by permission. For data on pages 69–70, from "Barring L.A. Students from Extracurricular Activities," copyright 1983, *Los Angeles Times*. Reprinted by permission. For data on page 83 on the Celtics-Lakers game, from "The Day in Sports," copyright 1985, *Los Angeles Times*. Reprinted by permission. For data on page 103 on highway speeds, from "Speeding on the Freeways," copyright 1983, *Los Angeles Times*. Reprinted by permission.